KS3

Science
**Practice
Test Papers**

Ages 11-14

CO_2

$NaCl$

H_2O

Jackie Clegg, Bob McDuell
and Tim Greenway

Contents

Sets
ABC

KEY STAGE 3
Levels 5–7
Introduction

Science

Introduction

Introduction

Instructions on using the Practice Test Papers

Understanding Assessment

At the end of Key Stage 3 (usually in Year 9 at the age of 14), teacher assessment is used to determine your level of attainment in subjects including English, Maths and Science. There are no national tests but assessments by your teacher will help them to determine your level of attainment (see page 7).

About these Practice Test Papers

This book contains three sets of practice test papers, which provide a means of parental or self-assessment that can be easily carried out at home. The papers will help you to evaluate an approximate level of attainment, highlight opportunities for further study and skills practice that will aid improvement, and record results to track progress. The instructions and guidelines in this Introduction provide guidance on how to use the papers for self-assessment.

The questions have been written by experienced teachers and are based on the programme of study for Key Stage 3. Important ideas may be revisited in order to ensure understanding and provide an opportunity for improvement.

Sets A, B and C each provide one complete assessment, consisting of two 60-minute tests. The two tests can be taken at different times, but try to complete them both within the same week. Take the tests at a time when you can work uninterrupted and do not feel tired.

You should complete Sets A, B and C towards the end of Key Stage 3. Make sure you leave a reasonable amount of time between each assessment – it is unrealistic to expect to see an improvement in just a few weeks. You will feel much more motivated if you wait for a while, because your progress will be more obvious.

If you want to re-use the practice test papers, you can write in pencil and then rub out your answers. However, do not repeat the same test paper too soon, otherwise you will remember the questions and your results will not be an accurate reflection of your abilities.

Before you start:
- find a suitable place to complete the tests – somewhere quiet, where you won't be disturbed
- make sure you have a pen, pencil, ruler, rubber and a clock or watch to time yourself
- turn off your mobile phone
- read the instructions on the front of the test paper carefully.

When completing the test papers:
- try to answer all of the questions and make sure you read them carefully
- write your answers in the spaces where you see the pencil icon
- keep an eye on the time – if you spend longer than an hour on the paper, your results will not accurately reflect your abilities.

When you have finished:
- use the answers and marks provided in the pull-out Answers and Mark Scheme to mark the test paper
- read the top tips on how to improve your performance and remember the key points
- add up the total number of marks.

Tips for the Top

Make sure you have a suitable place to do the test and have a pen, pencil, rubber and ruler.

Try all of the questions and write your answers where you see the pencil:

The number of marks is shown for each part of the question.

Remember to read the questions carefully.

Make your answers clearly legible. If you make a mistake, put a cross through it and write the correct answer clearly next to it. Use an eraser as little as possible.

Don't panic! These practice papers are meant to provide you with a guide to your progress and the level you are working at. They are not the be-all and end-all. If you cannot do a question, just go on to the next question and come back to it later if you have time.

Using your Marks to Assess Levels

Record your test marks in the progress grid below:

	Week Beginning (Date)	Test Paper 1	Test Paper 2	Total	Level
Set A					
Set B					
Set C					

When you have completed Test Paper 1 and Test Paper 2 for each set, add the two marks out of 75 together to give a total mark out of 150.

The table below will give you an indication of your level based on your marks:

Level 4 and below	Level 5	Level 6	Level 7
0–39	40–74	75–104	105–150

Remember that the level obtained in these tests may be different from the level that your teacher reports you are working at. This is because they can only test a limited range of skills and knowledge. Your teacher will have a better idea of your overall performance.

However, these tests will help you to identify areas of weakness that you can improve upon with a bit of hard work and extra study. This will help you to get a better mark on your next assessment test and progress at school.

Improving your Results and Making Progress

Go back through your test papers and make a note of all the questions that you got wrong. This will help you to identify topics that require further study.

If you want to improve your understanding and make progress, you need to be proactive! Use Study Guides and Workbooks for home study – they include lots of practice questions, which test your knowledge and reinforce what you have learned.

With a little bit of time and effort, when you take the next set of tests in the book you will achieve a higher mark. Remember to record the date alongside your marks in the grid above. This will allow you to track your progress over time and will help to build your confidence and a sense of achievement.

What do Levels Mean?

Attainment levels are used to measure your progress through Key Stages 1, 2 and 3.
They are concerned with your knowledge, skills and understanding of a subject.

There are eight levels and they each have a description, which sets out the skills, knowledge and understanding that you are expected to demonstrate at that level. The descriptions for Levels 1 to 8 get increasingly difficult.

Although there are eight levels, at Key Stage 3 you are generally expected to work between Levels 3 and 7, where Level 7 represents excellent knowledge, skills and understanding.

The table below shows the expected National Curriculum levels for 14 year olds.

Level	Aged 14
Level 1	
Level 2 Level 2c Level 2b Level 2a	
Level 3	Below average
Level 4	Below average
Level 5	At level expected
Level 6	At level expected
Level 7	Excellent
Level 8	Exceptional

As you can see, it is expected that a majority of 14 year olds will achieve Level 5 or 6 by the end of Year 9. If you achieve Level 7, it is a real success. A 14 year old who achieves Level 8 is working at an exceptionally high level. For comparison, a student who gains a GCSE grade C has achieved Level 7.

Your teacher will carry out regular assessments to ensure that you are working at an appropriate level and progressing at the expected rate. The test papers in this book support this process. Provided you follow the instructions and address any potential problems that the tests highlight, they will help to ensure you are always working to the best of your abilities.

Set
A

KEY STAGE 3
Levels 5–7

Test Paper 1

Science

Test Paper 1

Test Paper 1

Instructions:

- find a quiet place where you can sit down and complete the test paper undisturbed
- make sure you have all the necessary equipment to complete the test paper
- read the questions carefully
- answer all the questions in this paper
- write your answers where you see this symbol
- show all your working as marks may be awarded for this
- go through and check your answers when you have finished the test paper
- check how you have done using pages 105–106 of the Answers and Mark Scheme

Time:

This test paper is **1 hour** long.

Page	9	11	13	15	17	19	21	23	Max. Mark	**Actual Mark**
Score	…………	…………	…………	…………	…………	…………	…………	…………	75	…………

First name

Last name

1 Jason is using a periscope to see who is behind him.

Ben

Shaun

a) **On the diagram** below, draw a line to show how light passes through the periscope.

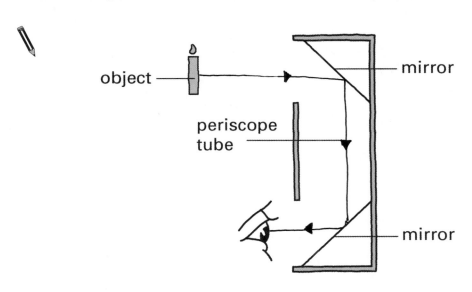

object

mirror

periscope tube

mirror

(3 marks)

Q1a

b) Jason can see Ben, but he cannot see Shaun.

Suggest why.

Because shaun is below the mirror. so Jason can't see him from reflection.

(1 mark)

Q1b

subtotal

c) The light ray reaches the mirror then bounces off again.

What is the name given to this movement of light?

Tick the correct box.

radiation ☐

reflection ☑

refraction ☐

(1 mark)

(Total 5 marks)

2 The female body has a menstrual cycle.

a) **At what age will a female usually start her menstrual cycle?**

Tick the correct box.

between 1 and 4 years ☐

between 10 and 16 years ☑

between 35 and 40 years ☐

between 60 and 65 years ☐

(1 mark)

The diagram shows the menstrual cycle.

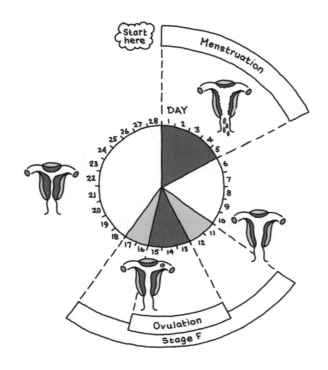

Use the information in the diagram to help you answer these questions.

b) i   For how many days does menstruation take place?

~~12-16~~   5   days   *(1 mark)*   Q2bi

    ii   What is meant by menstruation?

    Tick the correct box.

    An egg is released.   ~~☑~~

    Blood from the uterus wall is lost.   ☑

    Fertilisation takes place.   ☐

    The lining of the uterus starts to grow again.   ☐   *(1 mark)*   Q2bii

c) i   Between which days does ovulation take place?

    ~~And e~~   ~~An egg released from the ovary~~   *(1 mark)*   Q2ci

                    12 - 16 days

ii What is meant by ovulation?

Tick the correct box.

An egg is released.   ✓

Blood from the uterus wall is lost.   ☐

Fertilisation takes place.   ☐

The lining of the uterus starts to grow again.   ☐   *(1 mark)*

d) i Explain why fertilisation may take place at stage F.

An egg released from the ovary.

_____

_____ *(2 marks)*

ii Describe what happens to the sperm if fertilisation does not take place.

And is traveling along the narrow egg tube.

_____ *(1 mark)*

iii How does a female know if she is pregnant?

Postive Pregnancy Test.

_____ *(1 mark)*

iv How long does the female carry the baby (called the gestation period) before the baby is born?

40 weeks.

_____ *(1 mark)*

(Total 10 marks)

3   Four boys have a race over 100 metres.

Jimmy is younger, so he is given a 10 metre start. They all start at the same time.

The table gives their times for the race.

Boy	Time in seconds
John	15.0
Jimmy	18.0
Jamil	14.6
Jay	17.5

a) Write down the order in which they cross the finishing line. Start with the boy who finishes first.

    __14.6__   __15.0__   __17.5__   __18.0__   *(1 mark)*

Q3a

b) Calculate Jimmy's average speed in the race. Include the unit in your answer.

Speed = _____ 5 m/s. _____   *(3 marks)*

Q3b

(Total 4 marks)

4   The diagram shows two magnets repelling each other.

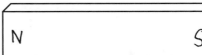

a) Label the poles on the right-hand magnet.   *(1 mark)*

Q4a

b) Draw an arrow to show the magnetic force acting on the right-hand magnet.   *(1 mark)*

Q4b

subtotal

c) Write down the name of a metal that can be used to make a magnet.

✎ _iron._ _____ (1 mark)

d) Circle the object that contains a magnet.

✎ (hairdryer)   **microscope**   **torch**   (1 mark)

(Total 4 marks)

5   Sarah and Paul shine a ray of light through a prism.

✎

a) The white light produces a spectrum as it passes through the prism. What is this process called?

✎ _Refraction._ _____ (1 mark)

b) On the diagram, write in the boxes to finish labelling the spectrum.   (1 mark)

c) Explain why the prism produces a spectrum when white light passes through it.

✎ _Because different colours travel in a different_

speed, red is the fastest. and violet is the slowest

_____ (3 marks)

(Total 5 marks)

6   The table gives information about three fuels that can be used to heat houses.

Fuel	State at room temperature	Substances produced on combustion		
		carbon dioxide	water	sulphur dioxide
coal	solid	✔	✔	✔
natural gas	gas	✔	✔	
wood	solid	✔	✔	

a)   Which fuel in the table is most difficult to store? Explain your answer.

Natural gas.

_____ (2 marks)

Q6a

b)   Which gas in the air is needed for these fuels to burn?

Circle the correct answer.

carbon dioxide   hydrogen   nitrogen   (oxygen)   (1 mark)

Q6b

c)   Burning large amounts of fossil fuels can cause major environmental problems.

Explain how burning fossil fuels contributes to global warming.

Because carbon dioxide is a greenhouse gas which absorbs

the heat in the atmosphere.

_____ (2 marks)

Q6c

d) Coal and natural gas supplies will eventually run out.

i Why should this not be a problem with wood?

Wood is renewable as fresh supplies to be grown. *(1 mark)*

ii When could there be a problem with wood?

shortage of supply as use exceeds replanting *(1 mark)*

(Total 7 marks)

7 Four metals, P, Q, R and S, are used in a series of reactions to find the order in the reactivity series.

The table summarises the results.

Solution	Add P	Add Q	Add R	Add S
nitrate of P	✗	✗	✗	✔
nitrate of Q	✔	✗	✔	✔
nitrate of R	✔	✗	✗	✔
nitrate of S	✗	✗	✗	✗

Key: ✔ reaction   ✗ no reaction

a) Arrange these four metals in order of **increasing** reactivity.

Least reactive ___ R S ___ P ___ R ___ Q ___ *(3 marks)*

b) Metal S reacts with steam to form a metal oxide and a colourless gas.

What is this gas?

Hydrogen. *(1 mark)*

c) T is another metal more reactive than Q. A reaction takes place when a powdered mixture of T and the oxide of Q were heated together.

What type of reaction is this and what are the products?

A displacement reaction.

Oxide of T & Q. _(2 marks)_

Q7c

d) T reacts when placed in a solution of the nitrate of R but does not react when placed in a solution of the nitrate of P.

What does this tell you about T?

T is between P & R in the reactivity series.

(2 marks)

Q7d

(Total 8 marks)

8   A 'fizzy pop' maker uses artificial dyes to colour drinks. Only some dyes can be used.

Scientists in a drinks company test samples of two drinks, E and F, from rival firms. They compare the results with the results from their own brand G.

The diagram shows the apparatus they use.

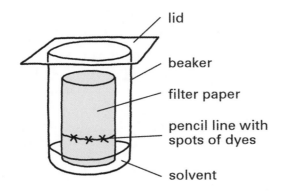

a) What is the name of the method they are using?

Choromatography. _(1 mark)_

Q8a

subtotal

b) What happens during the experiment?

At different rates.

Water moves up paper _____ *(2 marks)*

c) Why is it important that the spots on the filter paper are above the solvent at the start?

Otherwise. _____ *(1 mark)*

d) Why is it important that the line is a pencil line and not an ink line?

Because if it was ink, it can also destroyed the experienment. *(1 mark)*

e) The chart shows the results of the experiment.

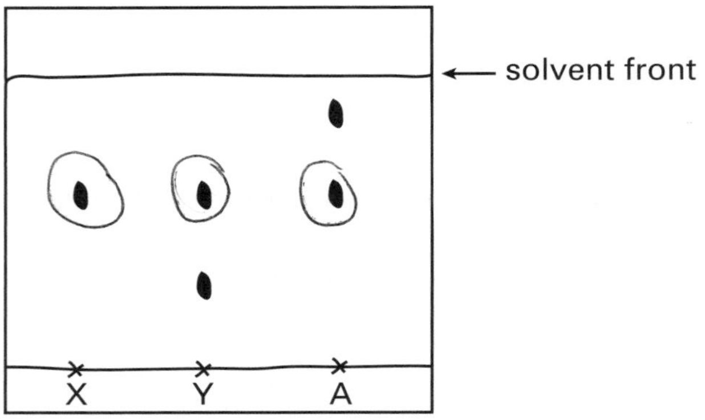

← solvent front

i   Which drink contains only one dye?

X. _____ *(1 mark)*

ii **On the chart** circle the dye which is in all the drinks.   *(1 mark)*

(Total 7 marks)

9 Grace investigated how the amount of light affects the number of bubbles given off by pondweed.

This is how she set up her apparatus.

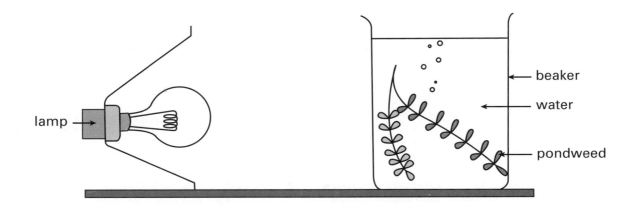

Grace left the apparatus set up for two minutes. She then started to count the number of bubbles formed in one minute intervals.

a) Suggest why she left the apparatus for two minutes before starting to count the number of bubbles.

Because it takes time for the lamp to heat up completely.

_____ *(1 mark)*

Q9a

Grace investigates the effect of increasing the amount of light by using extra lamps.

b) Grace wants to keep this a fair test.

   i Suggest **two** factors she will need to keep the same to make this a fair test.

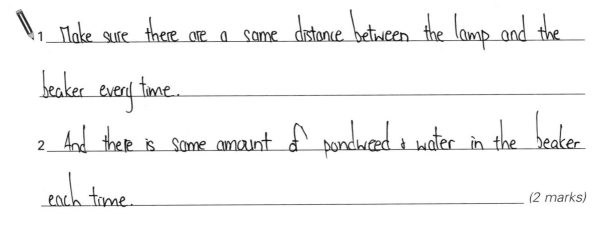

1 Make sure there are a same distance between the lamp and the beaker every time.

2 And there is same amount of pondweed & water in the beaker each time. *(2 marks)*

Q9bi

subtotal

ii   What is the **independent (input) variable** for this investigation?

_____ (1 mark)

c) The table shows her results.

Number of lamps	Number of bubbles in one minute
0	2
1	8
2	16
3	20
4	22

i   On the grid below, plot the points of these results.

The first one has been done for you.   (2 marks)

ii   Draw a smooth curve of best fit.   (1 mark)

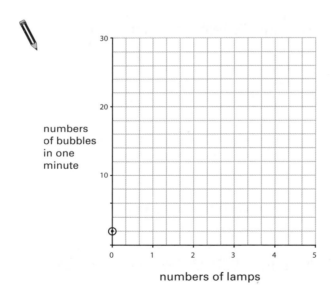

numbers of lamps

d) From your graph, estimate the number of bubbles with **5 lamps**.

_____ bubbles in one minute.   (1 mark)

e) Describe and explain the pattern shown by your graph of results.

🖊 _____

_____

_____

_____ *(2 marks)*

Q9e

(Total 10 marks)

10 The diagram shows the human digestive system.

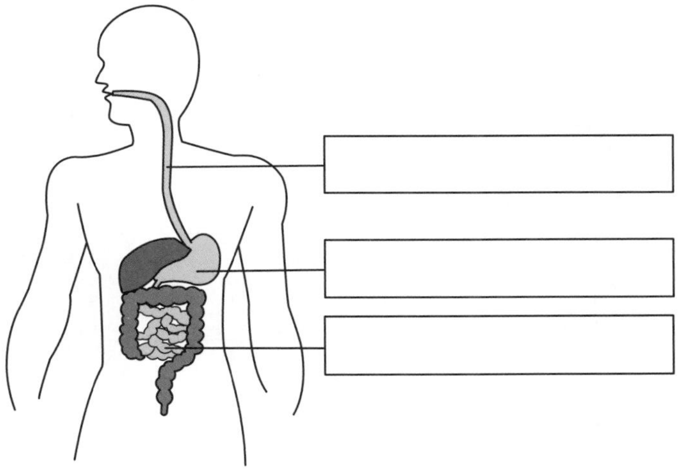

a) Finish labelling the diagram. *(3 marks)*

Q10a

Choose words from this list.

large intestine   oesophagus (gullet)   small intestine   stomach   liver

b) **On the diagram:**

i   Write a letter **D** to show where most digestion of food takes place. *(1 mark)*

Q10bi

ii   Write a letter **A** to show where most digested food is absorbed into the blood. *(1 mark)*

Q10bii

iii   Write a letter **E** to show where undigested food leaves the body. *(1 mark)*

Q10biii

c) Large molecules of food are digested (broken down) into smaller molecules.

Suggest why.

_____

_____ *(1 mark)*

d) The smaller molecules of digested food pass into the bloodstream through the walls of the small intestine. Describe how the small intestine is adapted for food absorption.

_____

_____

_____

_____

_____

_____ *(3 marks)*

(Total 10 marks)

11 The diagram shows a plant cell which is found in a leaf. The main cell organelles are shown.

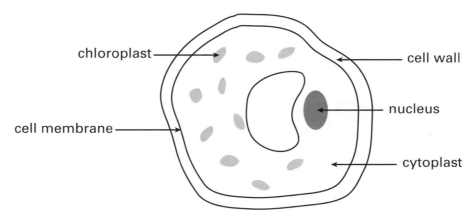

a) i   Which organelle, which is in this leaf cell, is not found in a plant root cell?

_____ *(1 mark)*

ii   Which two organelles shown on the diagram are not in animal cells?

_____

_____ *(2 marks)*

b) The five parts of the cell labelled on the diagram each have a different function.

In the table below, write the name of the cell organelle next to its function. One has been done for you.   *(2 marks)*

Organelle	Function
	Where chemical reactions take place
	Site of photosynthesis
Nucleus	Control centre of the cell
	Helps to keep the cell shape
	Controls which substances enter and leave the cells

(Total 5 marks)

END OF TEST

Set

A

KEY STAGE 3
Levels 5–7

Test Paper 2

Science

Test Paper 2

Test Paper 2

Instructions:

- find a quiet place where you can sit down and complete the test paper undisturbed
- make sure you have all the necessary equipment to complete the test paper
- read the questions carefully
- answer all the questions in this paper
- write your answers where you see this symbol
- show all your working as marks may be awarded for this
- go through and check your answers when you have finished the test paper
- check how you have done using pages 106–108 of the Answers and Mark Scheme

Time:

This test paper is **1 hour** long.

Page	25	27	29	31	33	35	37	39	Max. Mark	**Actual Mark**
Score	....	....	....	....	....	....	....	....	75	....

First name

Last name

1 Surinder pumps up a bicycle tyre.

When she has finished she notices that the pump has got warmer.

a) Describe where, and in what form, the energy was stored before it was transferred in pumping up the tyre.

_____

_____ *(1 mark)*

b) The gas particles inside the tyre exert a pressure on the inner walls of the tyre. Suggest how.

_____

_____ *(1 mark)*

c) When the air entering the tyres was warmed, the movement of the gas particles in the tyre changes. Suggest how.

_____

_____ *(1 mark)*

d) When the air in the tyre becomes hotter, the pressure rises. Give one reason why the pressure rises.

_____

_____ *(1 mark)*

e) The pressure in the tyre increases as Surinder forces more air into the tyre. Suggest why a larger amount of air increases the pressure in the tyre.

_____

_____ *(1 mark)*

(Total 5 marks)

2 The diagram shows a food web.

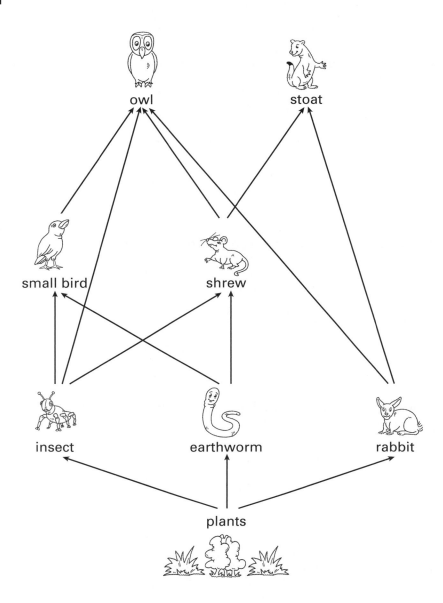

Use the information in the food web to help you answer the questions.

a) What **two** things do shrews eat?

_____

_____ _(2 marks)_

b) Name the producer.

_____ _(1 mark)_

c) i The owl is a predator.

Name **one other** predator.

____ *(1 mark)*

Q2ci

ii Name an animal that is both prey and a predator.

____ *(1 mark)*

Q2cii

iii Give **two** ways in which the owl is adapted to be a predator.

____

____

____ *(2 marks)*

Q2ciii

d) Describe the effects on the food web if there were no shrews present.

____

____

____

____

____ *(3 marks)*

Q2d

(Total 10 marks)

subtotal

3 Class 9A were investigating the effects of burning different masses of magnesium metal in air. The diagram shows the apparatus they used.

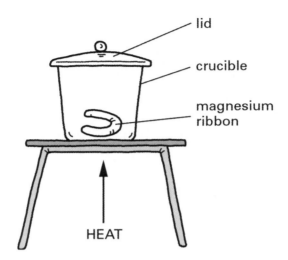

a) Explain why it is important to keep the lid on the crucible during the experiment.

(1 mark)

b) Complete the word equation for this reaction.

magnesium + _____ ⟶ _____ _____ _(2 marks)_

There are five groups, A–E. The results of the five groups are shown on the grid.

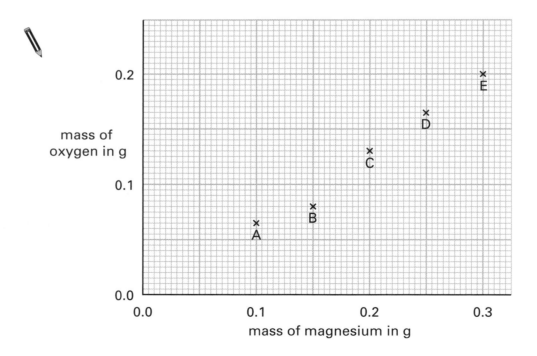

c) Draw the best line through these points. _(1 mark)_

d) i Which group seems to have produced a set of anomalous results?

_____ (1 mark)

ii Give two problems which might have occurred during this group's experiment.

_____

_____ (2 marks)

iii According to the graph, what mass of oxygen should have combined with this group's magnesium?

_____ (1 mark)

e) Just over two hundred years ago, scientists believed that combustion of any substance resulted in a loss of mass.

Lavoisier carried out many experiments burning different substances and finding the mass of reactants and products. He showed that combustion results in an increase in mass.

Sam says: "I think that there is a mistake in the experiment. Surely when I burn the magnesium in the air it loses mass because the metal has gone?"

Use the theory of combustion and the results of the groups' experiments to explain to Sam why he is wrong.

_____

_____

_____ (2 marks)

(Total 10 marks)

4   The three diagrams show the arrangement of particles in solids, liquids and gases.

A   B   C

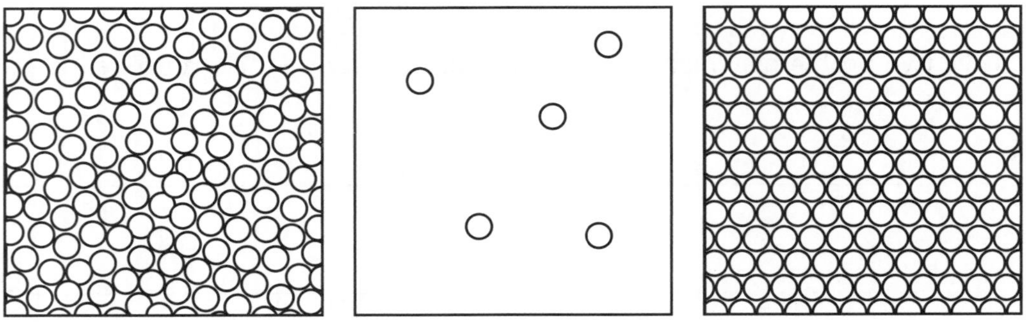

a) Which diagram shows a solid, which a liquid and which a gas?

solid   _____

liquid   _____

gas   _____   *(2 marks)*

b) Why does **C** have a higher density than **A** or **B**?

_____

_____ *(1 mark)*

c) Finish the table about changes of state.

From	To	Change of state	Is energy taken in or given out?
A	**B**	evaporation	taken in
C	**A**		
A	**C**		
B	**A**		

(4 marks)

(Total 7 marks)

5 Jane is out on a cycle ride.

In the diagram Jane is speeding up.

resistive force

driving force

a) How can you tell Jane is speeding up?

✏ _____ *(1 mark)*

Q5a

b) Draw arrows to show the forces acting on Jane and her cycle when she travels at a
    constant speed. *(1 mark)*

Q5b

✏

c) Jane pedals her bike along a level road. When she stops pedaling she slows down
    and then stops. Explain with reference to forces why the bike slows down and stops.

✏ _____

_____ *(2 marks)*

Q5c

(Total 4 marks)

6 The table shows the results of experiments to find the percentage of oxygen, nitrogen and carbon dioxide in three different places.

Gas	Percentage in sample of air (%)		
	Centre of city	City suburb	In the country
oxygen	17.5	18.0	19.8
nitrogen	79.9	79.9	79.9
carbon dioxide	0.05	0.03	0.02

a) One of the gases in the table is a compound.

Which gas is a compound and which elements make up this compound?

gas _____

elements _____ *(2 marks)*

b) What can you conclude about the percentage of nitrogen in each place?

_____ *(1 mark)*

c) Why does the carbon dioxide concentration need to be measured more accurately than oxygen or nitrogen?

_____ *(1 mark)*

d) i Where is the oxygen concentration lowest?

_____ *(1 mark)*

ii Why is this?

_____

_____ *(1 mark)*

e) Suggest another gas that might be found in the city centre in a higher concentration than in the country.

____ *(1 mark)* Q6e

f) i Name the process that converts carbon dioxide into oxygen.

____ *(1 mark)* Q6fi

ii In which of the three different places will more carbon dioxide be converted into oxygen? Explain your answer.

____

____

____ *(2 marks)* Q6fii

(Total 10 marks)

7 The drawing shows a bulldozer.

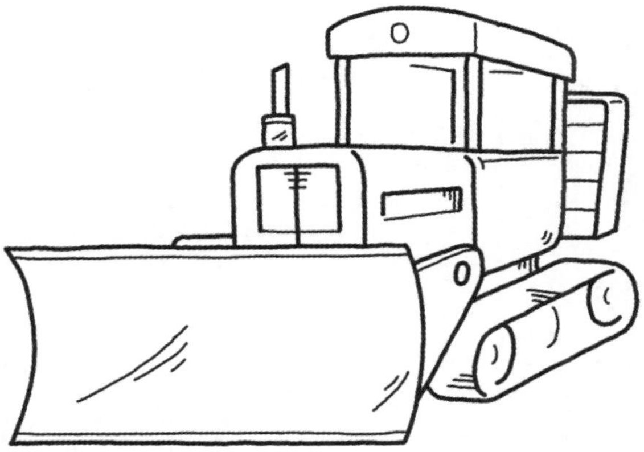

a) **On the diagram** draw an arrow to show the weight of the bulldozer. *(1 mark)* Q7a

subtotal

b) The bulldozer weighs 180 000 N. It has large caterpillar tracks. The area of the track in contact with the ground is 10 m².

  i Why does the bulldozer need large caterpillar tracks?

  _____ (1 mark)

  ii Calculate the pressure that the bulldozer exerts on the ground.

  Use the equation Pressure = $\dfrac{\text{Force}}{\text{Area}}$. Use the correct units in your answer.

  pressure _____ (3 marks)

  (Total 5 marks)

8 The graph shows a person's pulse rate before and after smoking a cigarette.

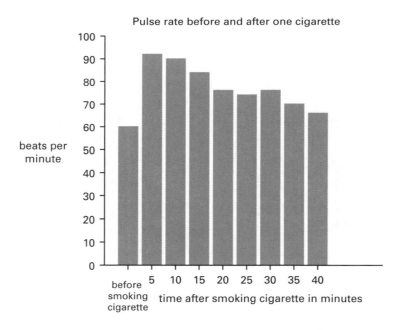

Pulse rate before and after one cigarette

a) What was the pulse rate before smoking a cigarette?

_____ beats per minute (1 mark)

b) By how beats per minute does the pulse rate increase in the first five minutes after smoking a cigarette?

Show how you worked out your answer.

_____ beats per minute   *(2 marks)*

c) Explain why the pulse rate increases after smoking.

_____

_____

_____ *(2 marks)*

d) Describe **two other** effects that smoking has on the body.

_____

_____ *(2 marks)*

(Total 7 marks)

9 Becky is investigating electromagnets.

She winds insulated wire around an iron nail and connects the wire to a power pack.

She then counts how many paperclips the electromagnet will pick up.

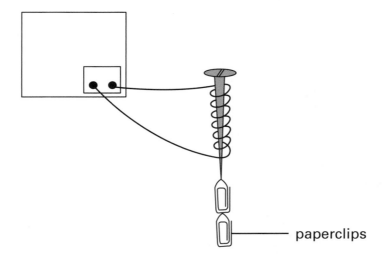

paperclips

a) Becky wants to increase the strength of her electromagnet.

   i Suggest **one** factor she could change to increase the strength of her electromagnet.

   _____

   _____ *(1 mark)*

   ii Becky wants to make sure this is a fair test.

   Write down **two** factors she should keep the same.

   1 _____

   2 _____ *(2 marks)*

   iii How will Becky know that the strength of her electromagnet has increased?

   _____

   _____ *(1 mark)*

b) Becky made this a fair test by controlling the other variables.

Explain why controlling the other variables makes it a fair test.

____

____

____ *(1 mark)*

Q9b

c) Becky's teacher tells her that she needs to make her results more **reliable**.

Describe what Becky must do to make her results more reliable.

____

____ *(1 mark)*

Q9c

d) **Write down one use for an electromagnet.**

____

____ *(1 mark)*

Q9d

(Total 7 marks)

10 Part of the reactivity series is shown below:

magnesium
zinc
iron
lead
copper
gold

a) **Why is gold found unreacted in the Earth but magnesium is not?**

____ *(1 mark)*

Q10a

subtotal

b) The word equation below is for a displacement reaction.

copper(II) sulphate + iron → iron(II) sulphate + copper

Why is the total mass unchanged during the reaction? Explain your answer.

_____

_____ (1 mark)

Q1

c) Which two of the following could be used to extract lead from lead(II) oxide?

Put two ticks in the correct boxes.

carbon dioxide ☐

hydrogen ☐

gold ☐

oxygen ☐

zinc ☐ (2 marks)

Q1

(Total 4 marks)

11 To help their customers choose the right plants, the Sunny Smile Garden Centre has added labels to them. The labels provide information about the best growing conditions for the plants.

The diagram shows the labels on two different plants.

Position: Partial shade
Humidity: Moist
Temperature: Keep warm

Position: Plenty of light
Humidity: Moist
Temperature: Keep warm

a) Plan an investigation to check if the labels were correct.

In your plan you must write about:
- the **one** factor you will change (the independent variable);
- **two** of the factors you will keep the same;
- the **one** factor you will observe (the dependent variable);

_____

_____

_____

_____

_____ *(3 marks)*

Q11a

b) The plant growing in the shade looks different from the plant growing in plenty of light.

   i   **Describe these differences.**

_____

_____ *(1 mark)*

Q11bi

   ii   **Explain how these differences help these plants to survive.**

_____

_____

_____ *(2 marks)*

Q11bii

(Total 6 marks)

END OF TEST

subtotal

Set
B

KEY STAGE 3
Levels 5–7

Test Paper 1

Science

Test Paper 1

Test Paper 1

Instructions:

- find a quiet place where you can sit down and complete the test paper undisturbed
- make sure you have all the necessary equipment to complete the test paper
- read the questions carefully
- answer all the questions in this paper
- write your answers where you see this symbol
- show all your working as marks may be awarded for this
- go through and check your answers when you have finished the test paper
- check how you have done using pages 108–109 of the Answers and Mark Scheme

Time:

This test paper is **1 hour** long.

Page	41	43	45	47	49	51	53	55	Max. Mark	**Actual Mark**
Score	....	....	....	....	....	....	....	....	75	....

First name ....

Last name ....

1 The graph shows the solubilities of potassium nitrate and sodium chloride in water at different temperatures.

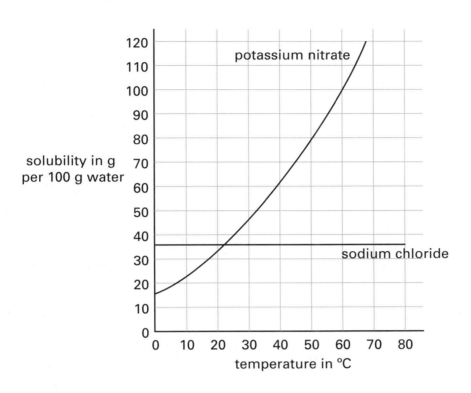

a) Use words from the list to complete the sentences.

insoluble   **soluble**   **solute**   **solution**   **solvent**

Sodium chloride dissolves in water and is said to be _____ in water.

A mixture of sodium chloride and water is a sodium chloride _____.

When sodium chloride is dissolved in water, sodium chloride is the

_____ and water is the _____.

(4 marks)

Q1a

b) What is the maximum mass of potassium nitrate that would dissolve in 50 g of water at 40°C?

_____ *(1 mark)*

Q1b

subtotal

c) How does the solubility of each substance change with temperature?

potassium nitrate _____

_____

sodium chloride _____

_____ (2 marks)

d) Jim carries out an investigation to out find the solubility of sodium chloride at 30°C.

According to the graph the expected value is 37 g per 100 g of water. Jim's investigation gives a value of 45 g per 100 g of water. His friends suggest some reasons for the difference.

Polly says it is because he had the wrong temperature.

Rosie says it is because he spilt some of the solid before he weighed it.

Sadie says it is because he had not evaporated off all the water.

Tim says it is because he did not dissolve the maximum possible amount of sodium chloride.

i   Who is correct?

_____ (1 mark)

ii   Explain your answer.

_____

_____

_____

_____ (3 marks)

(Total 11 marks)

2   Jade looks across the fields and can see a man chopping down a tree.

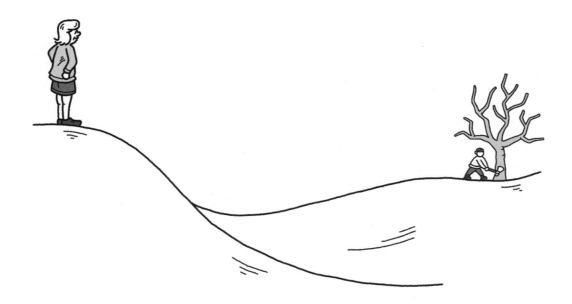

a)   Jade can see the man chopping down the tree before she hears the sound of the axe. It is a clear day with no wind.

     Suggest why.

_____

_____ *(1 mark)*

b)   In the next swing, the man swings his axe higher to chop the tree.

     What happens to the sound when the axe is moved from a higher distance?

     Tick the correct box.

the sound cannot be heard   ☐

the sound is louder   ☐

the sound is quieter   ☐

the sound is the same   ☐   *(1 mark)*

c) The diagram shows part of the human ear.

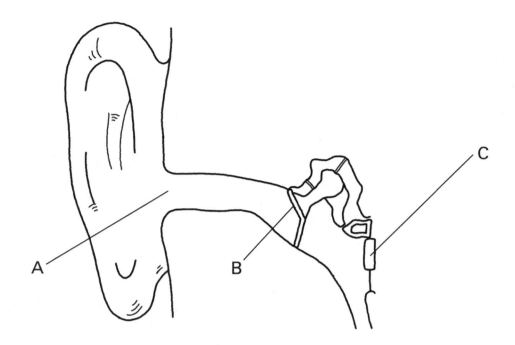

i Which of the labels **A**, **B** or **C** shows the eardrum?

Tick the correct box.

A ☐

B ☐

C ☐ *(1 mark)*

ii Describe what happens to our eardrums when sound reaches them.

_____ *(1 mark)*

d) Jade reads a leaflet that explains how some sounds can damage hearing.

Describe one type of sound that can affect hearing. State how it affects hearing.

type of sound _____

affect on hearing _____ *(2 marks)*

(Total 6 marks)

3   Tim carried out some experiments with four metals.

He wanted to put the metals in order of reactivity.

The results are shown in the table.

Metal salt solution	Add iron	Add zinc	Add magnesium	Add copper
iron(II) sulphate solution	no reaction	reaction	reaction	no reaction
zinc sulphate solution	no reaction	no reaction	reaction	no reaction
magnesium sulphate solution	no reaction	no reaction	no reaction	no reaction
copper(II) sulphate solution	reaction	reaction	reaction	no reaction

a)   Arrange the four metals in order of decreasing reactivity. Use the information in the table.

_____ _____ _____ _____   *(3 marks)*

Q3a

b) i   No reaction takes place when red-brown copper solid is added to colourless zinc sulphate solution.

Describe what you would **see** when zinc is added to copper(II) sulphate solution.

_____

_____   *(2 marks)*

Q3bi

   subtotal

ii   Write a word equation for this reaction.

+ ☐ → ☐ + ☐

(2 marks)

iii What type of reaction is taking place?

Circle the correct answer.

combustion   **displacement**   **neutralisation**   *(1 mark)*

(Total 8 marks)

4   The diagram shows the female reproductive system.

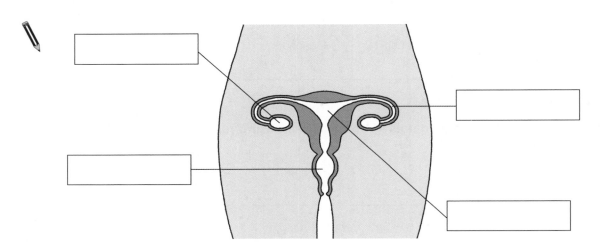

a) Label the diagram.

Choose words from the list.

ovary   **oviduct**   **uterus**   **vagina**   *(4 marks)*

b) On the diagram:

i   Write an **X** to show where sperm are deposited.   *(1 mark)*

ii   **Circle** the part where ovulation takes place.   *(1 mark)*

iii Write an **F** to show where fertilisation takes place.   *(1 mark)*

c) Sperm cells are adapted so they can move through the woman's reproductive system.

Describe two of these adaptations.

_____

_____ *(2 marks)*

Q4c

(Total 9 marks)

5 Indigestion can be caused by too much hydrochloric acid in the stomach.

a) **What is the job of the hydrochloric acid in the stomach?**

_____ *(1 mark)*

Q5a

b) Indigestion can be controlled by chewing and swallowing an antacid tablet.

The antacid contains a carbonate.

Explain why the carbonate helps control the indigestion.

_____

_____

_____ *(3 marks)*

Q5b

c) Jo has three different makes of antacid tablets.

She has some hydrochloric acid.

Explain how she could find out which make of tablets contains the most carbonate.

_____

_____

_____

_____

_____ *(4 marks)*

(Total 8 marks)

6   Look at the different energy sources.

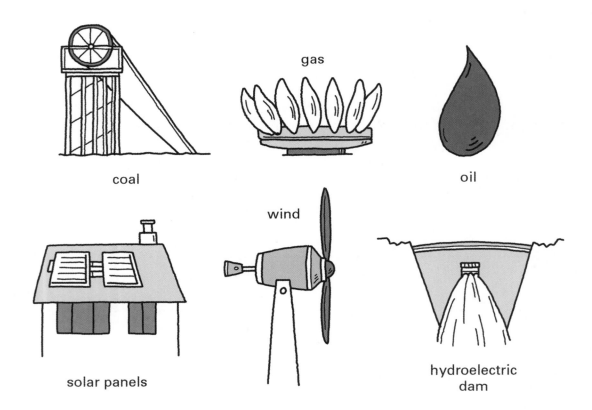

a) In many parts of the world fossil fuels are used to generate electricity. Give the names of three fossil fuels.

_____

_____ *(2 marks)*

b) Describe how fossil fuels were formed.

_____

_____

_____

_____ *(3 marks)*

c) More than half of the total fuels used in the world are biomass fuels.

   i   What is a 'biomass' fuel?

   _____

   _____ *(1 mark)*

   ii   Biomass and fossil fuels are both energy resources. What is the original source of this energy?

   _____ *(1 mark)*

   iii   How is this energy transferred from the source to the Earth?

   _____ *(1 mark)*

d) Fossil fuels are often described as non-renewable energy resources. Why are they called 'non-renewable'?

   _____

   _____ *(1 mark)*

e) There are advantages and disadvantages of burning different fuels.

   i Give one advantage of using biomass rather than fossil fuels as an energy resource.

   _____ *(1 mark)*

   ii Give one advantage of using fossil fuels rather than biomass as an energy resource.

   _____ *(1 mark)*

   iii Give one disadvantage of using both fossil fuels and biomass.

   _____ *(1 mark)*

                                                                    (Total 12 marks)

7   Michael plays football.

He has injured the ligaments in his knee.

The diagram below shows the structure of a joint.

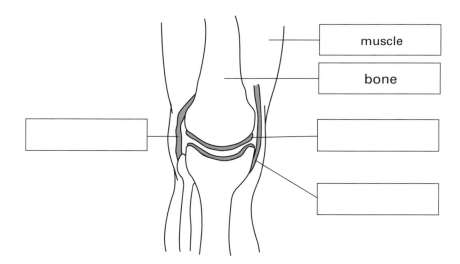

a) Finish labelling the diagram. Choose words from the list: *(3 marks)*

cartilage   ligament   tendon   synovial fluid

b) Michael has damaged the ligaments in his knee joint.

  i Suggest **one** way this damage will affect his knee joint.

  _____

  _____ (1 mark)

  The doctor thinks there may also be damage to the cartilage.

  ii Why is cartilage needed in joints?

  _____

  _____ (1 mark)

c) The diagram shows the muscles in Michael's leg.

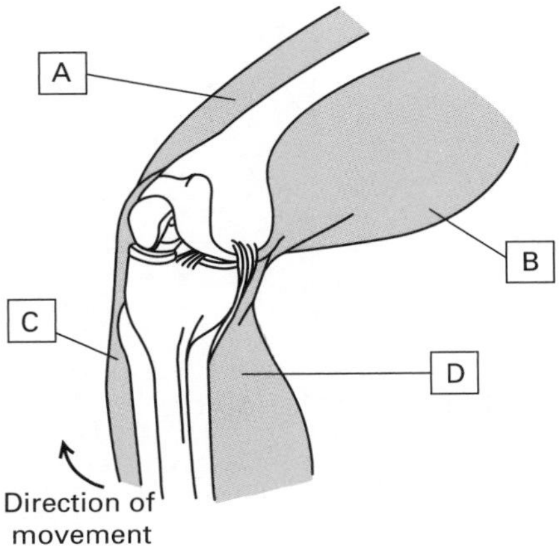

Direction of movement

The doctor asks Michael to lift the lower part of his leg.

  i How do the muscles move the leg in the direction shown by the arrow?

  Write the letter in the box that describes how the muscles work to lift the lower part of the leg.

  Choose from **A, B, C** or **D**.

  This muscle contracts. ☐

  This muscle relaxes. ☐   (2 marks) ii Explain why muscles need to work in pairs.

_____

_____ *(1 mark)*

(Total 8 marks)

8 Mollie and Ben sit on a seesaw and move about until it is balanced.

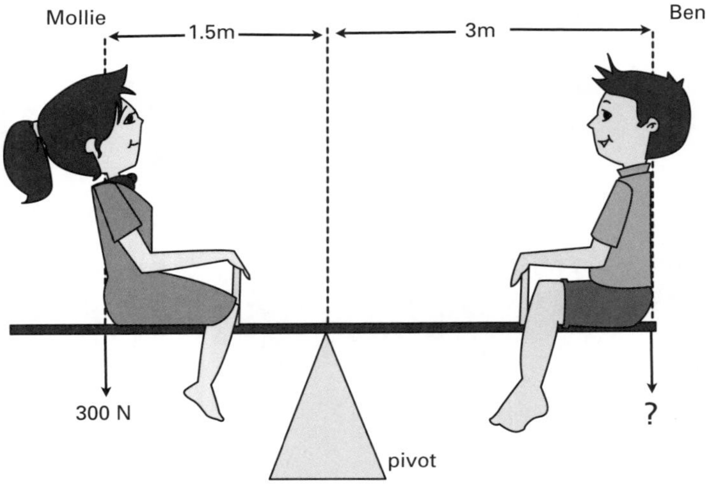

a) i Mollie weighs 300 N.

Calculate the turning moment produced by Mollie about the pivot.

_____ Nm *(2 marks)*

ii The seesaw is balanced.

Write down the turning moment produced by Ben about the pivot.

_____ Nm *(1 mark)*

b) Calculate Ben's weight. Give the unit in your answer.

Ben's weight is _____ *(2 marks)*

c) What is the size of the total force acting upon the pivot?

_____ N

(1 mark)

(Total 6 marks)

9 Asif was asked to find out whether an acid or an alkali was a stronger solution.

He put 5cm³ of alkali in a test tube.

He added acid 1cm³ at a time.

Each time he added more acid, he measured the pH of the solution.

His results are in the table.

Volume of acid added (cm³)	pH
Start (no acid)	10.5
1	10.5
2	10.0
3	9.5
4	7.5
5	5.0
6	4.0
7	3.5
8	3.5
9	3.0
10	3.0

a) Suggest a way in which Asif could have measured the pH of the solution during the experiment.

_____

_____ *(1 mark)*

b) To make this a fair experiment, Asif needed to control the other variables in the experiment.

Suggest two variables that he would need to control.

_____

_____ (1 mark)

c) Plot the results Asif obtained on the graph below.

Draw a suitable line of best fit. *(2 marks)*

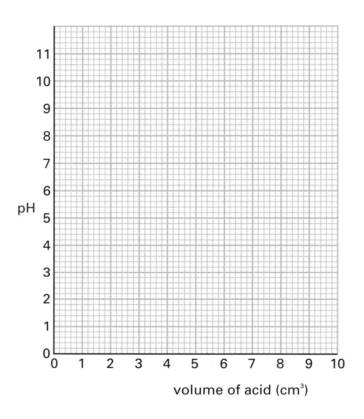

volume of acid (cm³)

d) How much acid did Asif need to make the solution neutral?

Circle the best answer.

Exactly 4cm³   **Between 4 and 5cm³**   **Exactly 5cm³**   **More than 5cm³**

(1 mark)

e) Which was stronger, the acid or the alkali?

Explain your answer.

_____

_____ *(2 marks)*

(Total 7 marks)

END OF TEST

Science

Test Paper 2

Instructions:

- find a quiet place where you can sit down and complete the test paper undisturbed
- make sure you have all the necessary equipment to complete the test paper
- read the questions carefully
- answer all the questions in this paper
- write your answers where you see this symbol
- show all your working as marks may be awarded for this
- go through and check your answers when you have finished the test paper
- check how you have done using pages 110–111 of the Answers and Mark Scheme

Time:

This test paper is **1 hour** long.

Page	57	59	61	63	65	67	69	71	Max. Mark	**Actual Mark**
Score	....	....	....	....	....	....	....	....	75	....

First name ....

Last name ....

1 Class 7B are investigating inherited variation.

Lisa and Jane record the eye colour of everyone in the class.

Here are their results.

Eye colour	brown	blue	grey	green	mixed
Number of pupils	7	14	0	3	4

a) Draw a bar chart to show the different eye colours in class 7B.   *(2 marks)*

One has been done for you.

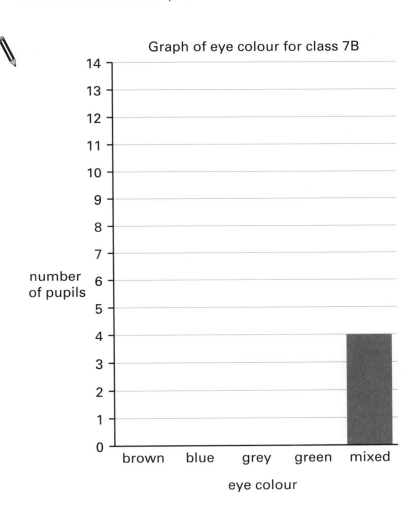

b) What is the most common eye colour?

_____ *(1 mark)*

c) Lisa and Jane have different ideas about their results.

Their teacher says not all of their ideas are correct.

Circle the correct letter for each idea.

Comment	Idea		
This idea is correct.	A	B	C
This idea is incorrect.	A	B	C
There are not enough results for this idea.	A	B	C

(2 marks)

d) i What is meant by the term 'inherited'?

_____

_____ *(2 marks)*

Their teacher tells them to investigate one other variation that is inherited.

ii Suggest one other variation they could investigate.

_____ *(1 mark)*

(Total 8 marks)

2 The headstones in a cemetery are made from different rocks.

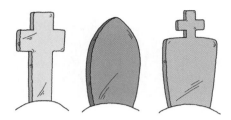

At one time, local rocks would be used. Today there is a wider choice including marble, granite and limestone.

a) Why were local rocks usually used?

_____ *(1 mark)*

b) Why was stone chosen rather than wood or metals?

_____ *(1 mark)*

c) Complete the table by using words from the list.

igneous   **metamorphic**   **sedimentary**

You may use the words once, more than once or not at all.

Rock	Type of rock
granite	
limestone	
marble	

(3 marks)

d) Sometimes, traces of ancient plants and animals can be found in certain types of rocks. These can be used to help date certain rocks.

   i   What are these traces of ancient plants and animals called?

_____ *(1 mark)*

ii   In which rock in the table would these traces **not** be found?

_____ (1 mark)

e)   The detail on a headstone wears down over a period of time. This occurs even when there is no atmospheric pollution.

i   Why is this?

_____ (1 mark)

ii   Explain why the carbon dioxide which is found in the atmosphere can have long-term effects on limestone.

_____

_____

_____ (2 marks)

f)   A headstone made of limestone has some cracks in it.

Explain fully how this headstone breaks down more quickly.

Diagrams may help your answer.

_____

_____

_____ (3 marks)

(Total 13 marks)

3 The diagram shows three circuits.

In each circuit there is a lamp and a motor.

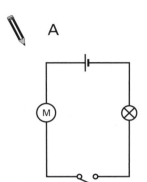 A   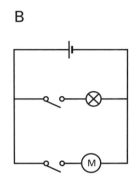 B   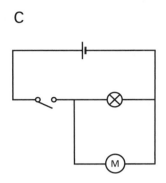 C

a) In which circuit are the lamp and motor in series?

_____ (1 mark)

Q3a

b) In which circuit can the lamp be switched on without switching on the motor?

_____ (1 mark)

Q3b

c) Use the same components to draw a circuit where the lamp is on all of the time but the motor can be switched on and off.

(1 mark)

Q3c

d) In Circuit A, the current passing through the motor is 0.5 A.

　i　What instrument is used to measure the current?

_____ (1 mark)

Q3di

subtotal

ii **On the diagram** mark with an **X** where this instrument should be connected.

(1 mark)

iii What current would be passing through the lamp?

_____ *(1 mark)*

e) In Circuit C, the current passing through the lamp and the motor is the same.

What information does this give?

_____ *(1 mark)*

(Total 7 marks)

4 Alex is calculating the volume of different objects.

a) Alex has a block 4 cm long, 3 cm wide and 2 cm high.

What is the volume of the block?

Use the correct unit in your answer.

_____ *(2 marks)*

b) Alex needs to use a measuring cylinder to calculate the volume of the pebble.

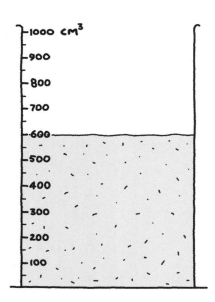
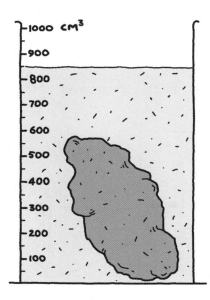

i What is the volume of the pebble?

_____ *(1 mark)*

ii Explain how you found the volume of the pebble.

_____

_____

_____ *(2 marks)*

(Total 5 marks)

5 Annette is making an electromagnet.

She uses an iron nail as the core and wraps insulated copper wire around it. She then connects a power supply to the two ends of the wire.

She then uses this electromagnet to pick up some steel paper-clips.

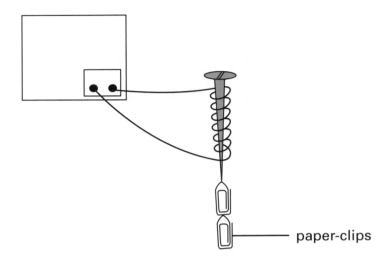

paper-clips

Annette makes a prediction about the strength of her electromagnet. She predicts that:

Reducing the number of turns of wire around the iron nail will reduce the strength of the electromagnet.

a) i What variable should she change to investigate her prediction?

_____ *(1 mark)*

ii Give one variable that she should keep the same.

_____ *(1 mark)*

iii How could she use the paper-clips to measure the strength of her electromagnet?

_____ *(1 mark)*

b) i Which size of paper-clips should Annette use to get the most accurate results?

Tick the correct box.

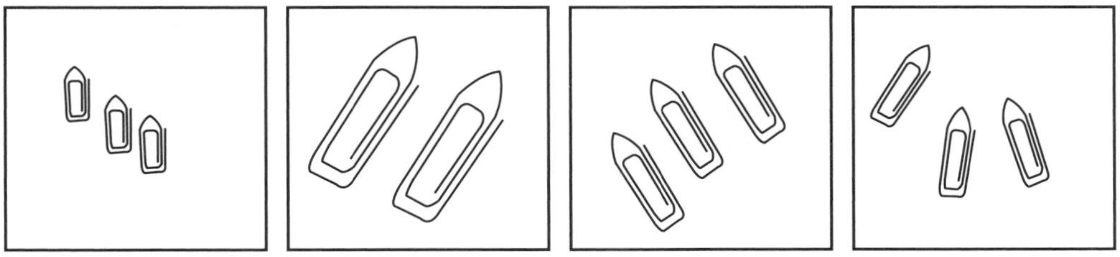

☐   ☐   ☐   ☐   *(1 mark)*

b) ii Why would this size provide the most accurate results?

_____ *(1 mark)*

(Total 5 marks)

6 Jack sits on a mat at the top of a helter-skelter and then slides down a chute around the outside.

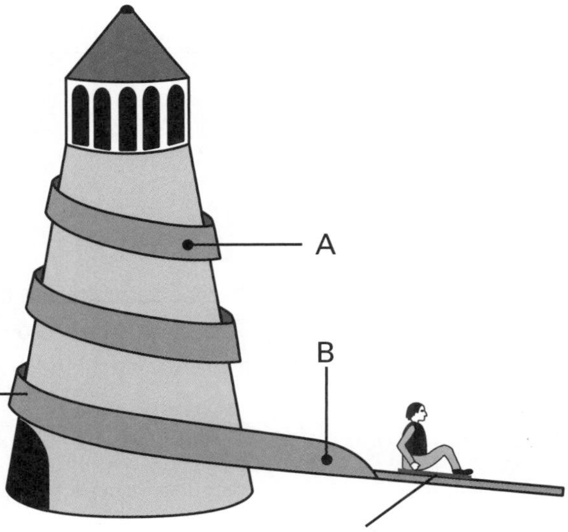

a) i Name **two** of the forces acting on Jack as he moves between point A and point B.

_____

_____ *(2 marks)*

subtotal

ii As Jack slides from point A to point B, the forces acting on him are balanced.

Describe what happens to Jack's speed when the forces acting on him are balanced.

_____

_____ *(1 mark)*

b) Jack goes back for a second go. This time he sits on a smooth cushion instead of a mat. He goes much faster.

Explain why he goes much faster on the cushion than on the mat.

_____ *(1 mark)*

c) On his next go Jack lies back on the cushion with his arms by his sides.

What happens to his speed? Explain why.

_____

_____ *(2 marks)*

(Total 6 marks)

7 Emily's friends are concerned that she smokes cigarettes. They carry out an experiment to show Emily the effect that smoking has on her body. They find Emily's average pulse rate, then Emily smokes a cigarette. They record Emily's pulse rate after smoking the cigarette.

The graph shows the effect that smoking one cigarette has on Emily's pulse rate.

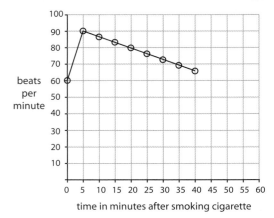

a) What was Emily's average pulse rate before smoking a cigarette?

_____ beats per minute   *(1 mark)*

b) Use the graph to estimate how many minutes it will take for Emily's pulse rate to return to normal.

_____ minutes   *(1 mark)*

c) Explain why this effect on pulse rate is dangerous for Emily's health.

_____

_____

_____ *(2 marks)*

d) It is the nicotine in cigarettes that affects pulse rate.

   i   Write down **one other** effect of nicotine.

_____

_____ *(1 mark)*

   ii   Write down the name of **one other** chemical produced when cigarettes are smoked and explain why it is dangerous to health.

Name of chemical _____

Why it is dangerous to health _____

_____

_____ *(2 marks)*

e) At the start of the experiment, Emily's friends find her average pulse rate.

i Describe how you would find the average pulse rate for a person.

_____

_____

_____

_____

_____

_____

_____ (3 marks)

ii Explain why it is better to find an average reading.

_____

_____

_____ (1 mark)

(Total 11 marks)

8 Many farmers spray chemicals on their fields. These chemicals are useful because they help crops to grow, but they can poison animals.

Sometimes these chemicals can enter a food chain. The diagram shows how these chemicals can be passed through an aquatic food chain.

a) What name is given to the chemicals that farmers use to help their crops grow?

_____ (1 mark)

Q8a

b) Explain how the chemicals can get into the river.

_____

_____ (2 marks)

Q8b

c) After a few years, the number of large fish in the river has gone down.

i   Explain why the toxic chemicals did not kill the smaller fish.

_____

_____ (2 marks)

Q8ci

ii   Suggest why the larger fish died from the toxic chemicals.

_____

_____ (1 mark)

Q8cii

iii Explain why the larger fish do not start to die until a few years after the toxic chemicals have been used.

_____

_____ (2 marks)

Q8ciii

(Total 8 marks)

subtotal

9 The table shows information about some planets in our Solar System and the length of their year.

Planet	Length of planet's year
Mercury	88 Earth days
Earth	365.25 Earth days
Jupiter	12 Earth years
Saturn	30 Earth years

a) Explain why the length of a year is different on each planet.

_____

_____ *(2 marks)*

b) Which of the planets in the table will have the **coldest** climate?

Explain why.

Planet: _____

Explanation: _____

_____ *(2 marks)*

c) Not all of the planets are listed in the table.

   i   Write down the name of the planet that is positioned between Mercury and Earth.

_____ *(1 mark)*

   ii   The length of year for Neptune is 165 Earth years.

   After which planet on the table would you list Neptune?

_____ *(1 mark)*

d) The length of a day is different on each of the planets. Explain why.

_____

_____ _(1 mark)_

(Total 7 marks)

10 There are a number of different organ systems in the human body. Some of these organ systems are shown on the diagrams.

| A | B | C | D | E |

The names of the five organ systems are given in the table. Next to each name, write the letter of the diagram which shows the organ system.

Name of organ system	Letter of diagram showing organ system
Circulatory system	
Digestive system	
Reproductive system	
Respiratory system	
Skeleton	

(5 marks)

(Total 5 marks)

END OF TEST

Set **C**

KEY STAGE 3
Levels 5–7

Test Paper 1

Science

Test Paper 1

Test Paper 1

Instructions:

- find a quiet place where you can sit down and complete the test paper undisturbed
- make sure you have all the necessary equipment to complete the test paper
- read the questions carefully
- answer all the questions in this paper
- write your answers where you see this symbol
- show all your working as marks may be awarded for this
- go through and check your answers when you have finished the test paper
- check how you have done using pages 112–113 of the Answers and Mark Scheme

Time:

This test paper is **1 hour** long.

Page	73	75	77	79	81	83	85	87	Max. Mark	**Actual Mark**
Score	....	....	....	....	....	....	....	....	75	....

First name

Last name

1   The diagram shows a cross-section through a flower.

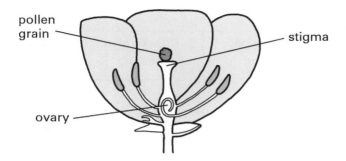

a)   The plant is reproducing.
     A pollen grain has landed on the stigma of the flower.
     The pollen and the egg cell need to join together.

     Below are five stages that lead to this process. They are in the wrong order.

     A   The nucleus of the pollen cell travels down the pollen tube and into the ovary.

     B   The pollen cell grows a pollen tube.

     C   The pollen cell nucleus and the egg cell nucleus join together.

     D   This forms the first cell of a new plant.

     E   The pollen tube grows down through the stigma and into the ovary.

     Fill in the boxes to show the right order.
     The first one has been done for you.

          B ☐ ☐ ☐ ☐   *(3 marks)*   ☐
                                                                                                          Q1a

b)   **What is the name given to the process at stage C?**

     Circle the correct answer.

          fertilisation   germination   pollination   *(1 mark)*   ☐
                                                                                                          Q1b

c)   The first cell that is formed at stage **D** continues to divide.

     What do the dividing cells form into before a new plant can be produced?

   _____ *(1 mark)*   ☐
                                                                                                          Q1c

                                                                                     (Total 5 marks)

2 Three solids, **X**, **Y** and **Z**, were heated.

Each solid was weighed before heating and after cooling to room temperature.

Solid	Appearance	Change on heating	Change after heating	Mass change
X	white solid	turns yellow	white solid	none
Y	purple crystals	black crystals	black crystals	decrease in mass
Z	red-brown solid	turns red	red-brown solid with a black coating	slight increase in mass

a) For each solid, decide if there is a physical change or a chemical change when it is heated. Put a ring around the correct answer each time.

Solid X: **Physical** / **Chemical**

Solid Y: **Physical** / **Chemical**

Solid Z: **Physical** / **Chemical**   *(2 marks)*

b) In one case oxygen is produced.

   i   Which of the three solids produces oxygen gas when it is heated?

   _____ *(1 mark)*

   ii   Describe how you would test to see if oxygen gas was produced in this case.

   _____

   _____ *(2 marks)*

c) Suggest why there is only a small increase in mass when Z is heated.

   _____ *(1 mark)*

(Total 6 marks)

3   Kelly and Becky are investigating friction.

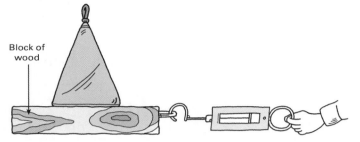

Block of wood

Kelly predicts that the weight on top of the block of wood will affect the friction.

To investigate this prediction, the girls measure the force needed to pull the wood when different weights are placed on top of the block of wood.

a)   State **two** factors they should keep the same to make their investigation fair.

1 _____

2 _____

(2 marks)

The table shows their results.

weight (N)	0	5	10	15	20	25
friction force (N)	15	21	26	30	37	42

b)   i   Use the data in the table to plot the points on the grid.   *(2 marks)*

The first two points have been done for you.

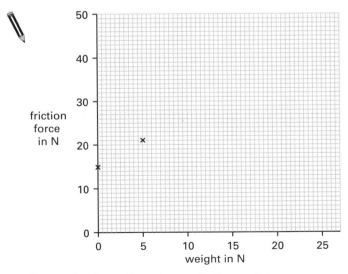

ii   Draw the best line through the points.   *(1 mark)*

c) Describe the relationship between the weight on the block and the friction.

_____

_____

_____ *(1 mark)*

d) Friction and weight are both types of force; they both use the symbol N.

What does the symbol N stand for?

Tick the correct box.

Neutral ☐   Nigel ☐

Newton ☐   Nought ☐   *(1 mark)*

(Total 7 marks)

4 Kate is trying to find out which disinfectant is the best to destroy microbes. She does the following:
- She leaves the agar plates open for 10 minutes to allow microbes to settle on the agar.
- She adds a different disinfectant to each agar plate.
- The plates are sealed, then left in a warm place for a few days.

a) i   Give one reason why we need to kill microbes.

_____

_____ *(1 mark)*

ii Sometimes it may be a disadvantage to kill microbes. Give one reason why.

_____

_____ *(1 mark)*

b) Describe **two** factors Kate must control to make this a fair test.

1 _____

_____

2 _____

_____ *(2 marks)*

Q4b

Here are Kate's results.

colonies of microbes

disinfectant
A

disinfectant
B

disinfectant
C

no
disinfectant

c) Why did Kate leave one agar plate without disinfectant?

_____

_____ *(1 mark)*

Q4c

d) Which disinfectant is the best to destroy microbes?

i disinfectant _____ *(1 mark)*

Q4di

ii Give a reason for your choice.

_____

_____ *(1 mark)*

Q4dii

subtotal

e) Kate's results are different from the class results.

Suggest how Kate could improve her experiment.

_____

_____ (1 mark)

f) In 1928, a famous scientist carried out a similar experiment and discovered antibiotics.

Circle the correct name of the scientist who discovered antibiotics.

Darwin   **Fleming**   **Pasteur**   (1 mark)

(Total 9 marks)

5   All electrical devices work because they convert electrical energy into other forms of energy.

a) For each of the devices below, state what forms of energy we want it to produce.

i   Electric lamp _____

ii Loudspeaker _____

iii Electric motor _____ (2 marks)

b) An electric lamp produces 5J of light energy for every 100J of electrical energy which is supplied to it.

i   What does the letter J stand for?

_____ (1 mark)

ii How much heat energy does the lamp produce at the same time?

_____ (1 mark)

iii What is the efficiency of the lamp? Underline the correct value.

0.05%   5%   50%   95%   100%   *(1 mark)*

(Total 5 marks)

6 Limestone and marble are two different types of rock. They both contain calcium carbonate. Calcium carbonate has the chemical formula $CaCO_3$.

a) Write down the names of the three elements found in calcium carbonate.

_____

_____ *(2 marks)*

Q6a

Limestone is an example of a sedimentary rock and marble is a metamorphic rock.

b) Describe how sedimentary rocks are formed from existing rocks.

_____

_____

_____

_____ *(3 marks)*

Q6b

c) Marble is an example of a metamorphic rock.

Describe how limestone is turned into marble.

_____

_____ *(2 marks)*

Q6c

(Total 7 marks)

7 The diagram below shows an outline of part of the Periodic Table of Elements.

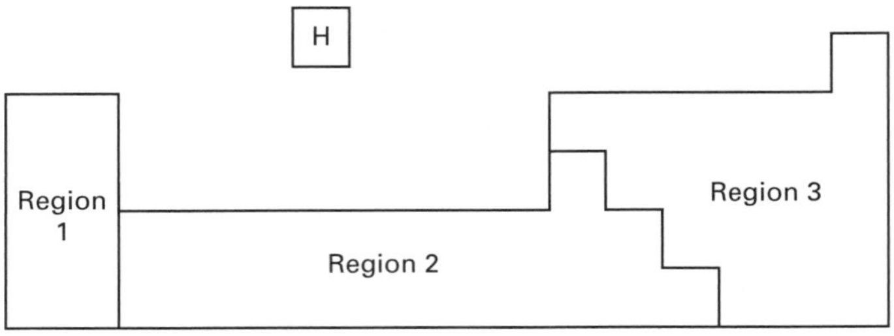

H

Region 1

Region 2

Region 3

a) Which element has the symbol H? _____ *(1 mark)*

b) Different elements are found in different parts of the Periodic Table. In which of the regions in the diagram of the Periodic Table are the following types of element found?

 i   Non-metals _____ *(1 mark)*

 ii Very reactive metals _____ *(1 mark)*

 iii Less reactive metals _____ *(1 mark)*

c) Suggest why aluminium sulphate is **not** found in the Periodic Table.

   _____

   _____ *(1 mark)*

d) An iron nail is placed into some blue copper(II) sulphate solution. A reaction takes place between the iron and the copper(II) sulphate and the nail changes colour.

 i   Suggest why the nail changes colour.

     _____ *(1 mark)*

 ii Complete the word equation for the reaction.

     iron + copper(II) sulphate ➔ [   ] + [   ] *(1 mark)*

(Total 7 marks)

8 Butane is a chemical compound which is often used as a fuel. Butane belongs to a group of compounds called hydrocarbons. The formula for butane is C_4H_{10}.

a) Write down the names of the two elements in butane.

 _____ and _____ *(1 mark)*

b) Butane is used as a fuel in a patio heater. Butane burns using oxygen in the air to form carbon dioxide and water.

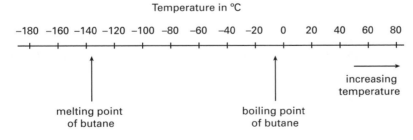

   i   Write a word equation for the combustion of butane.

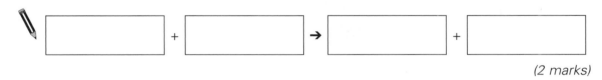

          [   ] + [   ] → [   ] + [   ]

                                                                                            (2 marks)

   ii   What environmental problem is caused by burning butane?

 _____ *(1 mark)*

c) The melting point and boiling point of butane are shown on the scale below.

Temperature in °C

−180 −160 −140 −120 −100 −80 −60 −40 −20 0 20 40 60 80

increasing temperature

melting point of butane

boiling point of butane

   i   At 20°C, is butane a solid, a liquid or a gas?_____ *(1 mark)*

   ii   At −10°C, is butane a solid, a liquid or a gas?_____ *(1 mark)*

d) Butane is usually stored as a liquid rather than a gas. Give one advantage of storing butane as a liquid rather than a gas.

_____

_____ (1 mark)

(Total 7 marks)

9 The diagram shows the human breathing system.

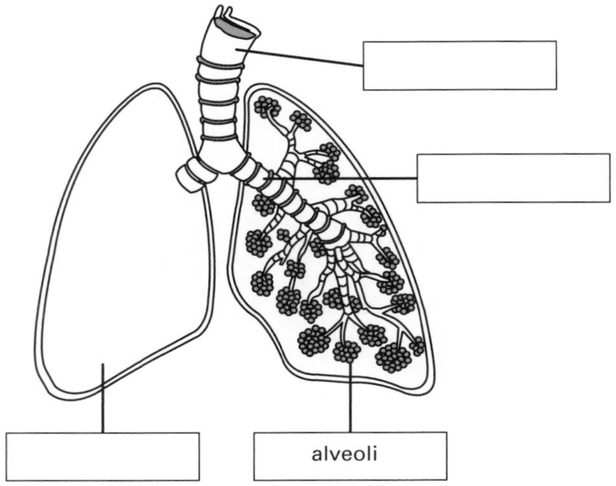

a) Finish labelling the diagram.   (2 marks)

Choose words from this list.

bronchioles   bronchus   lung   rib cage   trachea

b) Oxygen passes from the lungs into the blood.

Describe **one feature** of the alveoli that allows the efficient movement of gases to take place.

_____

_____ (1 mark)

c) **Why does the oxygen need to pass into the blood?**

____

____ *(1 mark)*

Q9c

d) Breathing and respiration are two different processes.

Describe some of the differences between them.

____

____ *(2 marks)*

Q9d

(Total 6 marks)

10 Joss is investigating electric circuits.

Joss uses identical batteries and bulbs to set up two different circuits, as shown in the diagrams below.

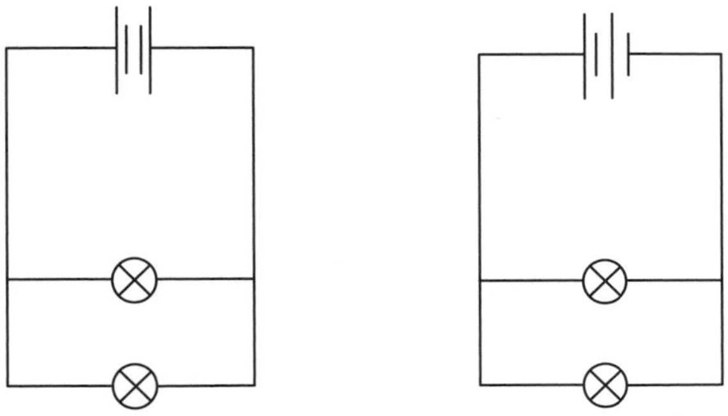

Circuit A   Circuit B

a) The lamps in circuit A will not light.

Give a reason.

____

____ *(1 mark)*

Q10a

subtotal

b) When Joss sets up circuit B, both of the lamps light up. Joss unscrews one of the lamps.

Describe what happens to the other lamp.

_____

_____ (1 mark)

c) What is the name given to this type of electric circuit?

_____ (1 mark)

d) Joss adds two ammeters to the circuit.

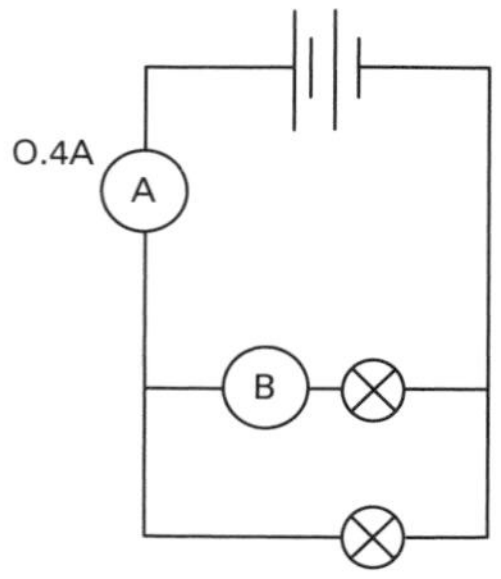

i What is the reading for Meter B?

_____ amps   (1 mark)

ii Why is this?

_____

_____ (1 mark)

e) The ammeter gives a reading in amps.

Describe what it is that the ammeter measures.

_____

_____ (1 mark)

(Total 6 marks)

11 Tom is investigating sound.

He makes an instrument by stretching different-sized
rubber bands around a wooden box.

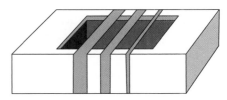

a) Tom plays the instrument by plucking the rubber bands. It makes a loud sound.

Describe what Tom must do to make a quiet sound.

_____

_____ *(1 mark)*

Q11a

b) Tom has used different thicknesses of rubber bands for his instrument.
As he plucks each rubber band, they each make a different sound.

The thick rubber band vibrates and produces a sound with a lower pitch.

Why does the thick rubber band have a lower pitch?

Tick the correct box.

The thick rubber band is a red colour. ☐

The thick rubber band vibrates more slowly. ☐

The thick rubber band does not vibrate. ☐

The thick rubber band vibrates more quickly. ☐ *(1 mark)*

Q11b

c) Tom plays his instrument near to a microphone that is connected to an oscilloscope.

The diagram shows the pattern made when he plucks
the thick rubber band. The sound shown in this pattern is:

Tick the correct box.

high pitch and loud ☐

low pitch and quiet ☐

high pitch and quiet ☐

low pitch and loud ☐ *(1 mark)*

Q11c

subtotal

d) Tom changes the rubber bands.
He puts two rubber bands of the same thickness onto the box.
They are a different length.

One rubber band is tight and one is loose.

Describe how the sound made by the tight rubber band is different from the sound made by the loose rubber band.

_____

_____ (1 mark)

(Total 4 marks)

12 In the 18th century, the disease smallpox was killing many people.

There was no cure for the disease.

A doctor named Edward Jenner wanted to prevent smallpox.

These notes describe how Edward Jenner developed a vaccine for smallpox.

A   Jenner noticed that milkmaids often caught cowpox but did not get smallpox.

B   Jenner had the idea that the cowpox prevented the milkmaids catching smallpox.

C   Jenner took pus from a cowpox sore of a milkmaid. He then made a small cut into the arm of a young boy. Jenner then rubbed the cowpox pus into the wound.

D   The young boy became ill with cowpox, but soon recovered.

E   Jenner then took some pus from the spots of a smallpox victim.

F   He made another small cut into the arm of the young boy and rubbed in the smallpox pus.

G   The young boy did not catch smallpox.

H   Jenner decided that having cowpox would stop you getting smallpox.

a) Write down the letter of the correct statement to answer these questions.
Choose your answers from **A, B, C, D, E, F, G** or **H**.

Which of the statements show:

i   Edward Jenner makes an **observation**. ☐

ii Edward Jenner makes a **hypothesis**. ☐

iii Edward Jenner makes a **conclusion**. ☐ *(3 marks)*

Q12a

b) **Describe how Jenner infected the young boy with cowpox.**

_____

_____ *(1 mark)*

Q12b

c) Jenner carried out his experiment on a young boy.

Suggest why.

_____

_____

_____ *(1 mark)*

Q12c

d) This method of **vaccination** has been so successful that doctors have managed to wipe out smallpox throughout the world.

Name one other disease that you can be vaccinated for.

_____ *(1 mark)*

Q12d

(Total 6 marks)

END OF TEST

subtotal

Set

C

KEY STAGE 3
Levels 5–7

Test Paper 2

Science

Test Paper 2

Test Paper 2

Instructions:

- find a quiet place where you can sit down and complete the test paper undisturbed
- make sure you have all the necessary equipment to complete the test paper
- read the questions carefully
- answer all the questions in this paper
- write your answers where you see this symbol
- show all your working as marks may be awarded for this
- go through and check your answers when you have finished the test paper
- check how you have done using pages 113–115 of the Answers and Mark Scheme

Time:

This test paper is **1 hour** long.

Page	89	91	93	95	97	99	101	Max. Mark	**Actual Mark**
Score	....	....	....	....	....	....	....	75	....

First name

Last name

1 The table shows information about the amount of air breathed in during different activities.

Activity	Litres of air breathed in per minute
sitting	
standing	7.8
slow walking	12.8
fast walking	23.0
running	45.0

a) i Plot the information on to the bar chart.

One has been done for you.

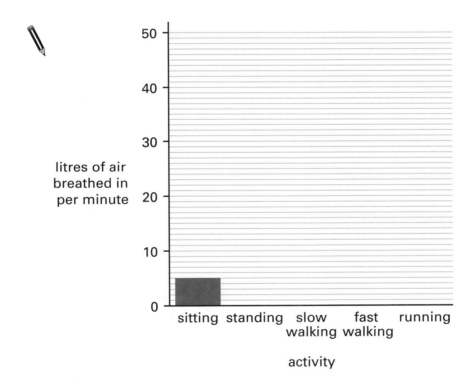

(2 marks)

Q1ai

ii How much air was breathed in whilst sitting?

Use the bar chart to find out the answer.

_____ litres per minute

(1 mark)

Q1aii

subtotal

b) Describe the relationship between the type of activity and the amount of air breathed in.

_____

_____

_____ (2 marks)

c) The air is used in the cells for respiration.

Finish the word equation for respiration.

Choose your words from the list.

carbon dioxide   **carbon monoxide**   **nitrogen**   **oxygen**

[   ] + glucose → [   ] + water

(2 marks)

d) i   Describe how oxygen is transported from inside the lungs to other cells in the body.

_____

_____

_____ (2 marks)

ii Explain why oxygen has to be transported to all body cells.

_____

_____

_____ (2 marks)

(Total 11 marks)

2 The following diagram represents part of a wave.

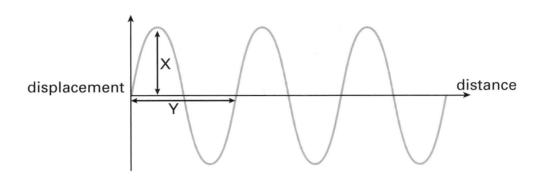

a) Choose words from the following list to name features X and Y on the diagram.

amplitude   frequency   velocity   wavelength

X _____

Y _____   *(2 marks)*

b) X-rays and light rays are two types of electromagnetic radiation. Complete the following table by naming the missing radiations shown by letter P and letter Q.

Gamma rays	X-rays	P	Light waves	Infra-red radiation	Microwaves	Q

P _____

Q _____   *(2 marks)*

c) All electromagnetic waves have properties in common. State **two** properties which are common to all electromagnetic waves.

1 _____

2 _____ *(2 marks)*

d) Ultrasound waves are used in hospitals for examining unborn babies while they are in the uterus.

   i   Describe what is meant by 'ultrasound'.

   _____ (1 mark)

   ii Give one advantage of using ultrasound instead of X-rays for examining an unborn baby.

   _____ (1 mark)

   iii Give one way in which an ultrasound wave is different from a light wave.

   _____ (1 mark)

   iv Give one way in which an ultrasound wave is similar to a light wave.

   _____ (1 mark)

e) X-rays can be used by doctors to look at broken bones inside our bodies.

   Explain how X-rays are able to produce pictures of bones inside the body.

   _____

   _____

   _____ (2 marks)

(Total 12 marks)

3 The table shows the times taken by some children to run 80 metres in a race.

Runner	Time taken
Becky	22 seconds
Chris	17 seconds
Faiza	20 seconds
Richard	25 seconds
Shaun	28 seconds

a) Who won the race?

_____ *(1 mark)*

Q3a

b) Calculate Richard's average speed. Include the unit in your answer.

Average speed = _____ *(3 marks)*

Q3b

c) Which runner was running at a speed of 2.9 m/s?

Show how you worked out your answer.

Runner _____ *(2 marks)*

Q3c

(Total 6 marks)

subtotal

4 Farmers breed animals to improve their usefulness. This is called selective breeding.

a) Suggest **two** features a farmer would want to breed into his animals.

1 _____

_____

2 _____

_____ (2 marks)

b) Here are four sentences about the selective breeding process.
   They are in the wrong order.

   A Farmers breed from these parents.

   B The process is repeated for many years.

   C When the offspring are grown, the farmers again select those with the best features.

   D Farmers choose the parents with the most useful features.

   Fill in the boxes to show the right order.

   The first one has been done for you.

   | D | | | | (3 marks)

c) Sometimes selective breeding is a process which takes many years. Explain why.

_____

_____ (2 marks)

(Total 7 marks)

5 a) State **two** ways in which a mixture is different from a compound.

1 _____

2 _____ (2 marks)

Ali draws five sketches of methods of separating mixtures.

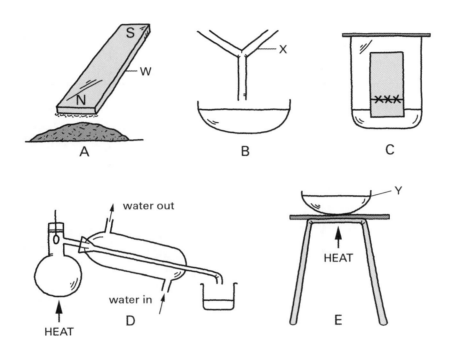

A   B   C

D   E

b) Three pieces of equipment, W, X and Y, are labelled on the diagrams.

Write down the names of the three pieces of apparatus.

W _____

X _____

Y _____ (3 marks)

c) Which method, A, B, C, D or E, could be used for each of the following separations? In each case give a reason why the method can be used.

i   Sand from a mixture of sand and salt solution.

_____

_____ (2 marks)

ii   Iron from a mixture of iron and sulphur powders.

_____

_____ (2 marks)

iii   Water from salt solution.

_____

_____ (2 marks)

(Total 11 marks)

6   Steve enjoys winter sports.

He has a snowboard and ice skates.

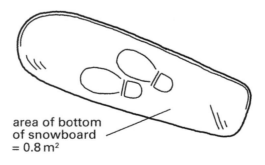

area of bottom of skate blades = 15 cm²

area of bottom of snowboard = 0.8 m²

a) When Steve walks on snow, his feet sink into the snow.

When Steve uses his snowboard, he does not sink into the snow.

Explain why.

_____

_____ (1 mark)

b) Steve's ice skates are very useful for moving around on ice.

Explain why.

_____

_____ (2 marks)

c) Steve weighs 600 N.

    i Calculate the pressure on the ground when Steve is on his snowboard.

       Use the equation Pressure = $\dfrac{\text{Force}}{\text{Area}}$. Give the unit in your answer.

                                    pressure = _____ (2 marks)

    ii Calculate the pressure on the ground when Steve is on his ice skates.

       Give the unit in your answer.

                                    pressure = _____ (3 marks)

(Total 8 marks)

7 Jamie is trying to float some different materials.

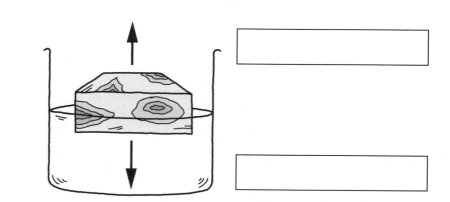

Jamie floats a block of wood on the water.
The arrows show the directions of two forces acting on the block of wood.

a) **On the diagram** label the forces.

(2 marks)

b) The wood is floating on the water.

What does this tell you about the forces acting on the wood?

_____ *(1 mark)*

c) Jamie thinks that whether a substance sinks or floats depends on its density.

The density of water is 1.0 g/cm³.

The density of the wood is 0.6 g/cm³.

The density of polystyrene foam is 0.03 g/cm³.

Predict whether the polystyrene will float or sink.

The polystyrene will _____

Give a reason for your answer.

_____

_____ *(1 mark)*

(Total 4 marks)

8 The diagrams represent the arrangement of the particles in a solid, a liquid and a gas.

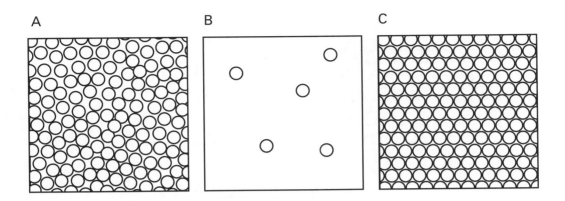

A   B   C

a) Which diagram represents the particle arrangement in...

i   a liquid? _____

ii a solid? _____

iii a gas? _____ *(1 mark)*

b) Describe what happens to the arrangement of the particles when...

i   solid is turned to a liquid.

_____

_____ *(2 marks)*

ii a liquid turns to a gas.

_____

_____ *(2 marks)*

c) Do the two changes in b) require energy or give out energy?

_____ *(1 mark)*

d) The diagrams below show how the particles are arranged in four substances, A, B, C and D.

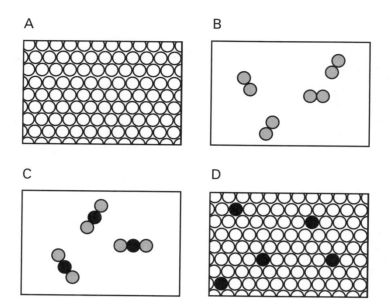

A   B

C   D

Each of the circles, ⚪ , 🔘 and ⚫ , shows an atom of a different element.

i Which substance is a compound? _____ (1 mark)

ii Which substance is a mixture? _____ (1 mark)

iii Which two substances are elements? _____

_____ (1 mark)

iv Which two substances could be good conductors of heat?

_____ (1 mark)

v Which substance could be carbon dioxide? _____ (1 mark)

(Total 11 marks)

9 The table shows the pH values of some substances.

pH value	example
1	dilute hydrochloric acid
2	
3	
4	
5	vinegar
6	
7	ethanol
8	
9	sodium hydrogencarbonate
10	
11	
12	
13	sodium hydroxide solution

a) Choose from this list.

    copper(II) sulphate solution   litmus solution   limewater   universal indicator

The pH value of a solution can be found using _____ *(1 mark)*

b) Choose from the table.

  i A neutral substance _____

  ii A strong alkali _____

  iii A weak acid _____   *(3 marks)*

c) Phenolpthalein is an indicator which is used in acid-alkali neutralisation. It is pink above pH8 and colourless below pH8.

Some phenolpthalein is added to a solution of sodium hydroxide. Vinegar is added slowly until the solution changes colour.

What is the colour change?

From _____ to _____ .   *(1 mark)*

(Total 5 marks)

END OF TEST

Notes

Notes

Notes

Answers and Mark Scheme
Science Set A Test Paper 1 Answers

1) a) Arrows clearly marked and in correct direction from object into eye. *(1 mark)*
   Continuous straight line from object to mirror reflection at both mirror surfaces and entry into eye *(2 marks)*
   b) Light travels in straight lines.
   OR
   The mirror is not pointing towards Shaun. *(1 mark)*
   c) reflection *(1 mark)*

2) a) Between 10 and 16 years *(1 mark)*
   b) i 5 *(1 mark)*
      ii Blood from the uterus wall is lost. *(1 mark)*
   c) i Between 12 and 16 days *(1 mark)*
      ii An egg is released. *(1 mark)*
   d) i An egg is released from the ovary. *(1 mark)*
      And is travelling along the narrow fallopian tube (egg tube). *(1 mark)*
      ii The sperm die **and** pass out of the woman's body. *(1 mark)*
      ***Examiner's tip** Your answer must not concentrate on fertilisation. You must consider what happens to the other sperm. Both points are needed in your answer.*
      iii Any **one** from:
      Menstruation stops occurring / Positive pregnancy test / There is an increase in weight or size. *(1 mark)*
      iv 9 months or 40 weeks *(1 mark)*

3) a) Correct order: Jamil, John, Jay, Jimmy *(1 mark)*
   b) Speed = distance ÷ time *(1 mark)*
      Speed = 90 ÷ 18 = 5 *(1 mark)*
      m/s *(1 mark)*
      ***Examiner's tip** In this question it is important to write down the relationship you are going to use. This gains the first mark. The second mark is for the calculation and not forgetting that Jimmy has a 10 metre start. The final mark is for the unit.*

4) a) The poles of the right-hand magnet should read NS. *(1 mark)*
   b) The arrow shows force direction from left to right. *(1 mark)*
   c) Any **one** from:
      Iron / Steel / Cobalt / Nickel *(1 mark)*
   d) hairdryer *(1 mark)*
      ***Examiner's tip** Any device containing an electric motor will contain a magnet.*

5) a) Refraction *(1 mark)*
      (***Accept:** dispersion*)
   b) yellow, green, blue *(1 mark in correct order)*
      ***Examiner's tip** If you need help remembering the order of colours in the spectrum, remember*

Richard Of York Gained Battles In Vain, where each first letter is the first letter of the colour.
   c) Different components (colours) travel at different speeds *(1 mark)*
      So are refracted by differing amounts. *(1 mark)*
      Red light is refracted least as it is travelling fastest
      OR
      Violet light is refracted most as it is travelling slowest. *(1 mark)*

6) a) Natural gas *(1 mark)*
      As a gas it needs to be stored in a sealed container under pressure. *(1 mark)*
   b) oxygen *(1 mark)*
   c) Carbon dioxide is a greenhouse gas. *(1 mark)*
      Which absorbs heat energy in the atmosphere. *(1 mark)*
      ***Examiner's tip** The question talks about environmental problems. Students often confuse these different environmental problems.*
   d) i Wood is renewable as fresh supplies can be grown. *(1 mark)*
      ***Examiner's tip** Answer must recognise that wood is a renewable resource.*
      ii Shortage of supply as use exceeds replanting. *(1 mark)*

7) a) S P R Q *(3 marks)*
      (One mark if Q is anywhere after R. One mark if R is anywhere after P. One mark if P is anywhere after S.)
   b) Hydrogen *(1 mark)*
   c) A displacement (or replacement) reaction. *(1 mark)*
      Oxide of T and Q. *(1 mark)*
   d) T is between P and R in the reactivity series. *(2 marks)*
      (T is above R – 1 mark; and below P – 1 mark)

8) a) Chromatography *(1 mark)*
   b) The solvent moves up the paper. *(1 mark)*
      (***Allow:** Water moves up paper.*)
      Different dyes move up different amounts or they move at different rates. *(1 mark)*
      (***Allow:** At different rates.*)
      ***Examiner's tip** It is important that you make two points here.*
   c) Otherwise the dyes would just dissolve in the solvent. *(1 mark)*
   d) Ink contains dyes and these might start to separate. *(1 mark)*
   e) i X *(1 mark)*
      ii A circle or circles (which appears in each) around the dye half way up. *(1 mark)*

9) a) To allow the plant to adjust to the difference in light *(1 mark)*
   b) i Any **two** from:
      Distance of lamp from beaker / Type of pondweed / Amount of pondweed / Volume of water / Temperature of water / Length of time to count bubbles / Two minutes at the start of each experiment / Colour of light / Background light *(2 marks)*
      ii Amount of light *(1 mark)*
      (Accept: light level)
   c) i 4 points plotted correctly *(2 marks)*
      3 or 2 points plotted correctly *(1 mark)*
      ii smooth curve *(1 mark)*
   d) answer between 22 and 24 *(1 mark)*
   e) Increasing the number of lamps (or the amount of light) increases the number of bubbles. *(1 mark)*
      The more light or lamps, the more photosynthesis takes place. *(1 mark)*

10) a) oesophagus (gullet), *(1 mark)*
       stomach, *(1 mark)*
       small intestine *(1 mark)*
       *(**Do not accept:** intestine)*

   b) i D on stomach *(1 mark)*
      ii A on small intestine *(1 mark)*
      iii E on anus (end of large intestine) *(1 mark)*
   c) Large molecules cannot be easily absorbed (into the blood or intestines) *(1 mark)*
   d) Any **three** from:
      It is very long so there is a large surface area / Presence of villi increase surface area / Walls thin and permeable / Good blood supply. *(3 marks)*

11) a) i Chloroplast *(1 mark)*
       ii Chloroplast *(1 mark)*
       Cell wall *(1 mark)*
   b) Cytoplasm
      Chloroplast
      Cell wall
      Cell membrane
      (All 4 correct for 2 marks; 2 or 3 correct for 1 mark)

Science Set A Test Paper 2 Answers

1) a) As chemical energy in Surinder
      OR
      As chemical energy in her muscles. *(1 mark)*
      *(**Accept:** As chemical energy in glucose **OR** named chemicals)*
   b) Any **one** from:
      Particles collide with the walls of the tyre / They hit the walls / Bounce off the walls / The particles exert a force acts on the area of the tyre walls. *(1 mark)*
   c) They speed up.
      OR
      They get faster. *(1 mark)*
   d) Any **one** from:
      Particles hit tyre wall more frequently / With more force / More collisions with tyre. *(1 mark)*
      *(**Do not accept:** More collisions / The particles move faster.)*
   e) There will be more frequent collisions with the tyre wall. *(1 mark)*
      *(**Accept:** More collisions with the tyre / The force applied by the particles increases.)*
      *(**Do not accept:** More collisions / Less space for the particles / There are more air particles to hit the tyre wall.)*

2) a) earthworms, *(1 mark)*
      insects *(1 mark)*
   b) plants *(1 mark)*

   c) i Any **one** of the following:
      stoats, small birds, or shrews *(1 mark)*
      ii **Either** of the following:
      small bird, shrew *(1 mark)*
      iii Good eyesight to see prey moving on the ground
      OR
      Fast dive in flight to catch prey *(2 marks)*
      Examiner's tip *A mark can be gained for either one explained adaptation or two adaptations stated. Remember to check the number of marks available and ensure you have written the same number of facts to match the mark.*
   d) Any **three** from:
      There would be more earthworms and insects.
      There would be more for the small birds to eat.
      There would be fewer plants for the rabbits.
      There would be fewer rabbits for the owls and stoats to eat, owls would need to eat more small birds, insects and rabbits, stoats would need to eat more rabbits, owls and stoats may leave the area to hunt somewhere else. *(3 marks)*
      Examiner's tip *A common mistake is to only describe effects from below the removed organism. To gain full credit, mention must be made about the effects above and below the position of missing shrews.*

3) a) To prevent any gases from moving in or
out. *(1 mark)*
b) oxygen *(1 mark)*
magnesium oxide *(1 mark)*
c) Straight line through origin **and** all points
except B *(1 mark)*
d) i B *(1 mark)*
ii Any **two** from:
Removing of the lid during the
experiment / Incomplete burning of
magnesium / Insufficient heating
(2 marks)
iii 0.1g *(Number **and** unit needed)* *(1 mark)*
e) Any **two** from:
The magnesium uses oxygen as it burns /
Combined mass of magnesium oxide /
Greater than mass of magnesium *(2 marks)*

4) a) solid – C liquid – A gas – B
*(All correct – 2 marks,
1 or 2 correct – 1 mark)*
b) The particles are closer together. *(1 mark)*
c)

From	To	Change of state	Is energy taken in or given out?
A	**B**	evaporation	taken in
C	**A**	**melting** *(1)*	**taken in**
A	**C**	**freezing** *(1)*	**given out**
B	**A**	**condensing** *(1)*	**given out** *(1)*

*(One mark for three energy changes in bold. The
mark in the right-hand column is scored only if all
three answers in this column are correct) (4 marks)*

5) a) The driving force is greater than the
resistive force. *(1 mark)*
b) Equal in size and opposite in direction
(1 mark)
c) Friction *(1 mark)*
Any **one** from:
Between the tyres and the road / Arising
from air resistance / Or moving parts of the
bike rubbing against each other. *(1 mark)*

6) a) carbon dioxide *(1 mark)*
carbon and oxygen (both required) *(1 mark)*
b) It is the same. *(1 mark)*
c) There is little of it.
OR
The changes in concentration are very
small. *(1 mark)*
d) i In the city centre. *(1 mark)*
ii More people, vehicles etc. using oxygen
up.
OR
There is no way the oxygen used can be
replaced. *(1 mark)*

e) Any **one** from:
Sulphur dioxide / Carbon monoxide /
Nitrogen oxides *(1 mark)*
f) i photosynthesis *(1 mark)*
ii In the country *(1 mark)*
More green plants. *(1 mark)*

7) a) vertical downward arrow from the centre
of the bulldozer *(1 mark)*
b) i Any **one** from:
To spread the weight over a larger area /
To reduce the pressure acting on the
ground / To prevent it sinking into the
ground. *(1 mark)*
ii 180 000 ÷ 10 = 18 000 *(2 marks)*
N/m² (**Accept:** *pascals*) *(1 mark)*
Examiner's tip *Remember – relationship,
calculation and then unit.*

8) a) 60 *(1 mark)*
b) Beats per minute after smoking = 92
92 – 60 *(1 mark)*
= 32 *(1 mark)*
Examiner's tip *It is always important to show
working out. If a simple error is made during the
calculation, some credit can be awarded for
evidence of working out.*
c) Less oxygen is reaching the cells, *(1 mark)*
so the body breathes faster to
compensate (or the heart pumps faster
to compensate). *(1 mark)*
d) Any **two** from:
Heart disease / Bronchitis / Emphysema /
Cancer. *(2 marks)*

9) a) i Any **one** from:
Increase number of coils / Increase size
of core / Use soft iron core / Increase
voltage/current *(1 mark)*
ii Any **two** from:
Voltage *(if not used as answer to part a) i)* /
Type of core *(if not used as answer to
part a) i)* / Length of wire / Size of
paperclips *(2 marks)*
iii A greater number of paperclips will be
picked up. *(1 mark)*
b) Only looking at the effect of the variable
that has been changed. *(1 mark)*
c) Increase number of readings
OR
Calculate an average reading *(1 mark)*
d) Any **one** from:
To move cars at a scrap yard / Used in
surgery to remove small pieces of iron /
Inside electric bells / relays / inside
speakers *(1 mark)*
Examiner's tip *An electromagnet is only
magnetic when the electric current is passing
around the circuit.*

10) a) Gold is unreactive and does not react with air, water etc., but magnesium is reactive. *(1 mark)*

b) No substances are gained or lost during the reaction *(1 mark)*

c) hydrogen and zinc *(2 marks)*

11) a) One set of plants in the shade and one set in plenty of light. *(1 mark)*
Any **two** from:
Keep the same / Size of pots / Material of pots / Type of soil / Volume of water given each day / Temperature / Humidity *(1 mark)*
Observe growth of plant *(1 mark)*

b) i The plant in the shade has leaves with a larger surface area.
(**Accept:** plant in shade has larger leaves, accept the reverse: plant in light has smaller leaves) *(1 mark)*

ii Any **two** from:
The plant in the shade has larger leaves to allow more sunlight to be absorbed /
To ensure photosynthesis can take place /
The plant in the light has smaller leaves to reduce water loss (transpiration) *(2 marks)*
Examiner's tip *Any question about plants and light will be expecting answers relating to photosynthesis.*

Science Set B Test Paper 1 Answers

1) a) i soluble *(1 mark)*
ii solution *(1 mark)*
iii solute; solvent *(2 marks)*
Examiner's tip *It is important to know and understand the meanings of the words in the list.*

b) 31 g *(1 mark)*

c) The solubility of potassium nitrate increases as temperature increases. *(1 mark)*
The solubility of sodium chloride is the same at all temperatures. *(1 mark)*
Examiner's tip *It is not enough to say the solubility of potassium nitrate increases. You must link it to temperature.*

d) i Sadie *(1 mark)*
ii Solubility of sodium chloride in water is not temperature dependent. *(1 mark)*
Rosie and Tim's suggestions would result in a higher value for solubility. *(1 mark)*
Sadie's suggestion leads to a lower result. *(1 mark)*

2) a) Light travels faster than sound. *(1 mark)*
Examiner's tip *Think about fireworks. You can see the firework explode in the sky before you hear the 'bang'.*

b) the sound is louder *(1 mark)*

c) i B *(1 mark)*
ii The eardrum vibrates. *(1 mark)*
Examiner's tip *'Vibrations' is a key word. Remember that sounds are made as a result of vibrations.*

d) Loud **OR** high pitch/frequency *(1 mark)*
can cause (temporary) deafness *(1 mark)*

3) a) magnesium, zinc, iron, copper *(3 marks)*
Examiner's tip *One mark if magnesium is anywhere before zinc. One mark if zinc is anywhere before iron. One mark if iron is anywhere before copper. You are not expected to learn the order of metals in the reactivity series but to work it out from the information given.*

b) i Blue copper(II) sulphate solution turns colourless. *(1 mark)*

Red-brown solid forms. *(1 mark)*

ii copper(II) sulphate + zinc ⟶ zinc sulphate (**Allow** zinc(II) sulphate) + copper *(2 marks)*
(One mark for left-hand side and one for right-hand side.)

iii displacement *(1 mark)*

4) a) *(4 marks)*

b) i X inside vagina *(1 mark)*
ii circle around an ovary *(1 mark)*
iii F on an oviduct *(1 mark)*

c) Any **two** from:
Sperm have a tail to propel them / Sperm are streamlined to help them move easily through the reproductive system / Sperm are small to help them move easily through the reproductive system *(2 marks)*
Examiner's tip *An easy way to remember the adaptations of sperm cells is to think of them as: 'many, minute and mobile'.*

5) a) Any **one** from:
To break down or digest food / To destroy bacteria (that enter the stomach with the food) *(1 mark)*

b) Carbonate reacts with acid *(1 mark)*
forming carbon dioxide *(1 mark)*
less acid reduces indigestion. *(1 mark)*

c) Measure out known quantity of acid or known quantity of tablet – mass used not number used. *(1 mark)*
Add tablets until stops fizzing / is neutralised or add acid until reaction stops. *(1 mark)*

Repeat with equal volumes of fresh acid
for each tablet brand.   *(1 mark)*
Smallest number used / smallest mass
used / greatest amount of acid neutralised
contains most carbonate.   *(1 mark)*

6) a) Any order: coal, gas, oil
(All 3 for 2 marks, 2 correct for 1 mark)
(Accept: *peat / methane)*
   b) Any **three** from:
   Dead plants and animals became covered
   in mud (or sand, or clay) / Oxygen could
   not reach the dead plants and animals / So
   decomposition could not take place /
   Pressure from overlying material forms
   fossils / Over millions of years.   *(3 marks)*
   Examiner's tip *It is important that you realise that
   the dead remains were covered and oxygen could
   not reach them for decomposition. If oxygen was
   available the dead remains would decompose
   rather than fossilise.*
   c) i Material from living things or plant
        matter.   *(1 mark)*
      ii The Sun / sunlight   *(1 mark)*
      iii (Electromagnetic) Radiation   *(1 mark)*
   d) They cannot be replaced / no more can be
      produced.   *(1 mark)*
   e) i Any **one** from:
        It is renewable / It is widely available / You
        can grow more of it / It will conserve
        fossil fuels.   *(1 mark)*
        (Do not accept: *It is cheaper to produce)*
      ii Any **one** from:
        It takes up less space / More suitable for
        use in vehicles / More energy per unit
        mass.   *(1 mark)*
        (Accept: *It is more concentrated / It can be
        transported more easily)*
      iii Any **one** from:
        Atmospheric pollution / Sulphur dioxide
        or carbon dioxide released / They release
        greenhouse gases.   *(1 mark)*

7) a) ligament (left-hand box), cartilage (top right-
      hand box), tendon (bottom right-hand box),
      (3 marks)
   b) i Bones will move out of position as knee
        joint is bent   *(1 mark)*
      ii Reduces friction
         OR
         Stops bones rubbing together   *(1 mark)*
   c) i A   *(1 mark)*
        B   *(1 mark)*

ii Muscles can only pull the bone
   OR
   As one muscle pulls the other relaxes
   and becomes longer   *(1 mark)*
Examiner's tip *Muscles can only pull bones,
they cannot push bones. This is why they need
to work in pairs. One muscle pulls the bone
one way and the other muscle will pull it back.*

8) a) i weight x distance from pivot,
         300×1.5 *(1 mark)*
         450   *(1 mark)*
      ii 450   *(1 mark)*
   b) turning moment ÷ distance from pivot
      $450 \div 3$
      150N   *(1 mark for number, 1 mark for unit)*
   c) $450 + 150 = 600$ *(1 mark)*
   Examiner's tip *When asked to carry out a
   calculation, you must write out the formula and
   show all of your working out.*

9) a) Meter   *(1 mark)*
   (Accept: *data logger)*
   (Do not accept: *colour change)*
   b) Any **two** from:
   Temperature / Amount of stirring / Agitation
   / Time needed   *(1 mark)*
   c) All points correctly plotted: see graph.
                                         (1 mark)
   Smooth curve of best fit through all points:
   see graph.   *(1 mark)*

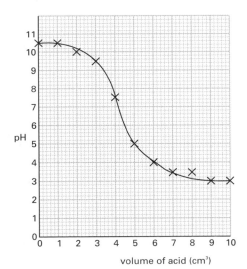

   d) Between 4 and $5cm^3$ *(1 mark)*
   e) Acid   *(1 mark)*
   Any **one** from:
   Less than $5cm^3$ of acid needed to
   neutralise $5cm^3$ of alkali / When equal
   volumes of acid and alkali had been mixed
   the pH was less than 7   *(1 mark)*

Science Set B Test Paper 2 Answers

1) a) *(All 4 bars correct – 2 marks, 2 or 3 bars correct –*
   1 mark)
   b) blue *(1 mark)*
   c) C
   B
   A
   (All 3 correct – 2 marks, 1 or 2 correct – 1 mark)
   Examiner's tip *It is important to understand that*
   a lack of results can prevent a definite conclusion.
   The more results, the more reliable the
   conclusion.
   d) i Passed on from parents, *(1 mark)*
   by genes. *(1 mark)*
   ii Any **one** from: Hair colour / Height /
   Shoe size / Length of finger / Ear lobes
   attached or unattached / Can roll tongue /
   Left handed or right handed etc. *(1 mark)*

2) a) Any **one** from:
   To minimise costs of transport / Difficult to
   travel with heavy rocks / Availability. *(1 mark)*
   b) Rocks do not rot or corrode away like wood
   or metals. *(1 mark)*
   (Accept: *stronger / last longer)*
   (Do not accept: *it looks good)*
   c) igneous *(1 mark)*
   sedimentary *(1 mark)*
   metamorphic *(1 mark)*
   d) i Fossils *(1 mark)*
   ii Granite or igneous rock *(1 mark)*
   e) i Weathering and/or erosion of rocks.
   (1 mark)
   ii Any **two** from:
   Carbon dioxide is soluble / Dissolves in
   water / To produce carbonic acid or acid
   rain / Acid reacts with the limestone
   rocks / Wearing them away. *(2 marks)*
   Examiner's tip *The action of carbonic acid on*
   limestone is an example of chemical
   weathering.
   f)

   water gets into crack *(1 mark)*
   water expands when it freezes *(1 mark)*
   splits rock apart *(1 mark)*
   Examiner's tip *Full marks are possible for a good*
   diagram clearly labelled.

3) a) A *(1 mark)*
   b) B *(1 mark)*

   c) *(1 mark)*

   d) i Ammeter *(1 mark)*
   ii X can be marked anywhere in the circuit.
   (1 mark)
   iii 0.5 A *(1 mark)*
   Examiner's tip *The current in a series circuit is*
   the same all round the circuit.
   e) The lamp and the motor must have the
   same resistance. *(1 mark)*
   Examiner's tip *If the resistance of the motor was*
   greater than the lamp, the current passing through
   the motor would be less than the lamp.

4) a) $4 \times 3 \times 2$ *(1 mark)*
   24 cm³ *(1 mark)*
   b) i 250 (cm³) *(1 mark)*
   ii The pebble displaced the water; *(1 mark)*
   the volume of the pebble is equal to the
   amount of water displaced. *(1 mark)*
   (the difference between the second
   reading and the first)

5) a) i The number of turns **or** coils of wire
   (1 mark)
   ii Any **one** from:
   The current / The length **or** thickness **or**
   material of the wire **or** coil *(1 mark)*
   (Accept: *the voltage* **or** *power, the*
   circumference of the coil.)
   (Do not accept: *the number of paper-clips.)*
   iii Any **one** from:
   Count the number of paper-clips picked
   up / Measure their mass (weigh them)
   (1 mark)
   (Accept: *the more clips the stronger the*
   magnet)
   b) i

   ✓ ▢ ▢ ▢

   (1 mark)
   (if more than one box is ticked, award no mark)
   ii Greater precision is possible with
   smaller increases in (mass) increments
   (1 mark)
   (Do not accept: *they are smaller)*

6) a) i Any **two** from:
   Gravity or weight / Friction / Reaction /
   Air resistance *(2 marks)*
   (Accept: *upthrust or drag)*
   (Do not accept: *centrifugal force* **or** *centripetal*
   force **or** *g-force)*

ii Any **one** from:
Constant speed / Steady speed / It stays
the same   *(1 mark)*
(**Accept:** *it is the same or it does not change*)

b) Friction is less   *(1 mark)*
(**Do not accept:** *it is smoother or it is slippery*)

c) It increases   *(1 mark)*
(**Accept:** *he goes more quickly*)
Because there is less air resistance **or**
friction   *(1 mark)*
(**Accept:** *he is streamlined or aerodynamic*)

7) a) 60   *(1 mark)*

b) Accept answer between 45 and 50
minutes   *(1 mark)*

c) The increase in pulse rate is due to the
heart beating faster;   *(1 mark)*
this puts a strain on the heart.   *(1 mark)*

d) i Nicotine is addictive   *(1 mark)*
ii Tar   *(1 mark)*
clogs lungs and causes lung disease /
cancer   *(1 mark)*
OR
Carbon monoxide   *(1 mark)*
stops the red blood cells supplying
oxygen to the body   *(1 mark)*

e) i Any **three** from:
Use your fingers at a point where an
artery comes close to the surface of the
skin (wrist, neck) / Count the number of
ripples (pulse beats) for one minute (or
part of a minute and multiply to make up
to one minute) / Repeat (usually three
times) / Add the total of readings
together / Divide the total by the number
of times a reading taken (usually three)
(3 marks)

Examiner's tip *If an answer is worth 3 marks,
you must check that you have included 3
important points. It is often useful to write
down your 3 important points before you start
to write your answer. Cross them out as you
write about each one. This way you will not
forget an important point.*

ii An average is more reliable than just one
reading.   *(1 mark)*

8) a) Fertilisers   *(1 mark)*
(**Accept:** *manure or named chemicals in fertilisers,
e.g. N,P,K*)

b) Any **two** from:
Chemicals sprayed onto fields / Chemicals
soluble in water / Chemicals washed off
land into river   *(2 marks)*

c) i The smaller fish only take in small
amounts of toxic chemcials;   *(1 mark)*
this is not sufficient to kill the smaller
fish.   *(1 mark)*

Examiner's tip *It is easier to remember the
rule that the concentration of toxic substances
increases as it moves through the food chain.*

ii Larger fish eat the smaller fish and take
in more toxic chemicals.
OR
Larger amounts of chemicals
accumulate inside the body of the fish,
causing it to die.   *(1 mark)*

iii The larger fish eat lots of smaller fish
over a few years.   *(1 mark)*
It takes time for the chemicals to
accumulate inside the fish to a high
enough level to cause death.   *(1 mark)*

9) a) Any **two** from:
A year is the time taken for the planet to
orbit once around the Sun / Different
planets take different times to orbit the
Sun / The longer the orbital line, the longer
the year.   *(2 marks)*

b) Saturn   *(1 mark)*
It is furthest away from the Sun.   *(1 mark)*

c) i Venus   *(1 mark)*
ii After Saturn   *(1 mark)*

d) Any **one** from:
A day is the time taken for the planet to
rotate/spin once on its axis / Different
planets take different amounts of time to
rotate on their axis.   *(1 mark)*
Examiner's tip *Make sure you understand the
difference between 'orbit' and 'rotate'. When a
planet orbits the Sun it moves around the Sun.
When a planet rotates it spins on its axis.*

10)

Name of organ system	Letter of diagram showing organ system
Circulatory system	C
Digestive system	D
Reproductive system	B
Respiratory system	A
Skeleton	E

(5 marks)

Science Set C Test Paper 1 Answers

1) a) B E A C D   *(3 marks)*
   (E anywhere before A – 1 mark; A anywhere before C – 1 mark; C anywhere before D – 1 mark)
   b) fertilisation   *(1 mark)*
   c) A seed   *(1 mark)*

2) a) Solid X – Physical
   Solid Y – Chemical
   Solid Z – Chemical   *(All 3 for 2 marks; any 2 for 1 mark)*
   b) i Y   *(1 mark)*
   ii Glowing splint   *(1 mark)*
   relights   *(1 mark)*
   c) Reaction only takes place on surface of red-brown solid.   *(1 mark)*
   Examiner's tip *You are not expected to try to identify these solids.*

3) a) Any **two** from:
   Surface being pulled over / Size of wood block / Type of wood / Same force meter.
        (2 marks)
   b) i

   All 4 points plotted correctly   *(2 marks)*
   3 or 2 points plotted correctly   *(1 mark)*
   ii Straight line through most of the points.
        (1 mark)
   Examiner's tip *Don't just join all the points. This is not acceptable. The line is to show the pattern or trend. Some of the points may not be correct, so an incorrect trend would be shown if points were joined up.*
   c) Increasing the weight increases the friction **OR** vice versa   *(1 mark)*
   d) Newton   *(1 mark)*

4) a) i Some microbes cause disease and illness.   *(1 mark)*
   ii Microbes can be useful (to humans).
        (1 mark)
   (**Accept:** *Any specific example, e.g. they help digestion / sewage treatment / decay)*
   b) Any **two** from:
   Left open in same place / Left open for the same amount of time / Same amount of disinfectant / Same temperature / Same length of time to incubate.   *(2 marks)*
   Examiner's tip *Questions asking about controlling factors to ensure a fair test are common in tests.*

   c) As a control
   OR
   To check that microbes would grow on the agar   *(1 mark)*
   d) i C   *(1 mark)*
   ii No microbes were growing on the agar.
        (1 mark)
   e) By adding microbes to the agar at the start
        (1 mark)
   (by taking a swab of soil and wiping it onto the agar).
   f) Fleming   *(1 mark)*

5) a) i Light
   ii Sound
   iii Kinetic or movement
   (All 3 for 2 marks; 2 correct for 1 mark)
   b) i Joule(s)   *(1 mark)*
   ii 95 Joules (***Accept:*** *95)*   *(1 mark)*
   iii 5%   *(1 mark)*

6) a) Calcium, carbon and oxygen
   (Two marks for all three correct. One mark for two correct)
   b) Any **three** from:
   Existing rocks are broken down by weathering and/or erosion / Into small particles/sediments / Sediments are transported by rivers / Sediments are deposited / Sediments are compressed / Sediments are buried.   *(3 marks)*
   c) Any **two** from:
   By the action of heat and pressure / Under the Earth's surface / When the limestone is subducted.   *(2 marks)*

7) a) Hydrogen   *(1 mark)*
   b) i Region 3   *(1 mark)*
   ii Region 2   *(1 mark)*
   iii Region 1   *(1 mark)*
   c) Ammonium sulphate is a compound (and the Periodic Table contains only elements)
        (1 mark)
   Examiner's tip *The word compound must be used to gain the mark.*
   d) i Copper is deposited on the surface of the nail.   *(1 mark)*
   ii iron(II) sulphate + copper   *(1 mark)*
   Examiner's tip *The order of these chemicals is not important but both are needed to gain the mark.*

8) a) carbon and hydrogen *(both required)*
        (1 mark)
   b) i butane + oxygen ➜ carbon dioxide + water   *(2 marks)*
   (One mark for left-hand side and one mark for right-hand side)
   ii Global warming   *(1 mark)*

c) i gas *(1 mark)*
   ii liquid *(1 mark)*
d) Much more can be stored in the same volume
   OR
   There are risks of explosion with high pressure storage. *(1 mark)*

9) a) trachea (top),
      bronchus (2nd from top),
      lung (bottom left)
      (2 marks for all 3 correct; 1 mark if 2 correct)
   b) Any **one** from:
      Wall of alveoli only one cell thick / Alveoli surrounded by network of capillaries (good blood supply) / Shape of alveoli increases surface area / Inside wall of alveoli moist *(1 mark)*
   c) So blood can carry oxygen around the body/to all of the cells. *(1 mark)*
   d) *1 mark for* breathing:
      – Breathing moves air into the lungs
      – Breathing moves air out of the lungs
      1 mark for respiration:
      – Takes place in cells
      – Reaction between oxygen and glucose
      – Releases energy
      – Produces water and carbon dioxide
      (2 marks)
      Examiner's tip *The processes of breathing and respiration are often confused. It is easier to remember that breathing gets the air into the body and respiration takes place inside every cell in your body. B comes before R.*

10) a) Cells are facing each other. *(1 mark)*
    b) Stays light *(1 mark)*
    c) Parallel *(1 mark)*
    d) i 0.2 *(1 mark)*

ii The current is shared between each route in a parallel circuit. *(1 mark)*
e) The passage of electric current *(1 mark)*
   Examiner's tip *In a parallel circuit the electric current is divided equally as it passes through each route. If there had been four routes in this circuit the current in each route would be 0.1 A.*

11) a) Pluck the rubber bands more gently
       OR
       Not pluck the rubber bands so hard *(1 mark)*
    b) The thick rubber band vibrates more slowly. *(1 mark)*
    c) low pitch and loud *(1 mark)*
    d) The tight rubber band will be a higher pitch. *(1 mark)*
       Examiner's tip *When looking at the patterns formed by oscilloscopes you need to remember the louder the sound the higher the wave pattern, the higher the pitch the closer together the wave pattern.*

12) a) i A *(1 mark)*
       ii B *(1 mark)*
       iii H *(1 mark)*
    b) He took pus from a cowpox sore and rubbed it into a wound. *(1 mark)*
    c) The young boy had less chance of already having smallpox.
       OR
       The young boy was less likely to have had any diseases. *(1 mark)*
    d) Any **one** from:
       Polio / Mumps / Measles / Rubella / T.B. *(1 mark)*
       Examiner's tip *There is a lot of reading for this question. It is often a good idea to have a quick look through the questions first before you start reading the text. This way you know what information you are looking for.*

Science Set C Test Paper 2 Answers

1) a) i

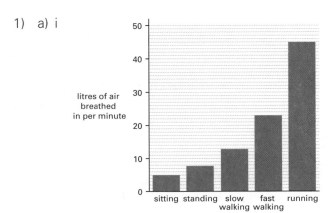

All four plotted correctly – 2 marks.
2 or 3 plotted correctly – 1 mark.

ii 5 *(1 mark)*
b) The greater the activity, *(1 mark)*
   the greater the amount of air breathed in. *(1 mark)*
   Examiner's tip *When asked to describe a relationship it is a good idea to think of relationships as "er–er relationships". This helps to reinforce the idea that you need to consider two factors. The factors are usually greater, slower, stronger, faster, etc.*
c) oxygen *(1 mark)*
   carbon dioxide *(1 mark)*
d) i Any **two** from:
     Oxygen diffuses through the alveoli (air sacs/lungs) / Into the bloodstream / The bloodstream transports the oxygen around the body. *(2 marks)*

ii Any **two** from:
Oxygen needed for respiration / To release energy from food / Respiration happens in all body cells. *(2 marks)*

2) a) X = amplitude *(1 mark)*
   Y = wavelength *(1 mark)*
   b) P = Ultra violet *(1 mark)*
   (**Accept**: UV)
   Q = Radiowaves *(1 mark)*
   (**Do not accept:** TV or UHF)
   c) Any **two** from:
   Travel at same speed / Travel at speed of light / Can be reflected / Can be refracted *(2 marks)*
   d) i Any **one** from:
   High frequency sound waves / Waves with frequency higher than 20KHz / Waves with frequency above threshold of human hearing *(1 mark)*
   Examiner's tip *Your answer must refer to frequency to get the mark*
   ii Any **one** from:
   X-rays can cause cancer/mutations/birth defects / Ultrasound is safe *(1 mark)*
   iii Any **one** from:
   Travels slower / Lower frequency / Shorter wavelength / Longitudinal not transverse wave *(1 mark)*
   iv Can be reflected *(1 mark)*
   e) Any **two** from:
   Pass through skin and muscle / Absorbed by bone / Produces shadow picture of bones / X-rays cause film to be exposed *(2 marks)*

3) a) Chris *(1 mark)*
   b) Speed = distance ÷ time *(1 mark)*
   = 80 ÷ 25 = 3.2 *(1 mark)*
   m/s *(1 mark)*
   c) Shaun (must be slower than Richard) *(1 mark)*
   80 ÷ 28 = 2.9 m/s *(1 mark)*
   (**Accept** 2.8)
   Examiner's tip *You need to compare the results and estimate which runner it might be. The second mark can only be awarded if the answer is supported with the calculation.*

4) a) Any **two** from:
   Increase in milk yield / Thicker fleece / Disease resistance / Greater muscles / Increase in egg yield *(2 marks)*
   (**Accept other reasonable answers**)
   b) D A C B *(3 marks)*
   c) With any generation there is a slight change *(1 mark)*
   It takes many generations before the required features are consistently reproduced in the offspring. *(1 mark)*

5) a) Any **two** from:
   Compounds are produced in chemical reactions / Compounds need a chemical reaction to separate them / Mixtures can be separated by physical means / Compounds have fixed compositions (mixtures do not) *(2 marks)*
   b) W – magnet *(1 mark)*
   X – (filter) funnel *(1 mark)*
   Y – evaporating basin *(1 mark)*
   c) i B *(1 mark)*
   Sand remains in filter paper.
   OR
   Salt solution goes through filter paper.
   OR
   Salt dissolves in water and sand does not. *(1 mark)*
   ii A *(1 mark)*
   Iron is attracted to a magnet.
   OR
   Sulphur is not attracted to a magnet. *(1 mark)*
   iii D *(1 mark)*
   Water boils off when heated, and steam is condensed.
   OR
   Salt remains in flask. *(1 mark)*

6) a) The snowboard has a larger surface area. *(1 mark)*
   b) The ice skates have a small area; *(1 mark)*
   OR high pressure;
   that causes a groove in the ice. *(1 mark)*
   c) i Pressure = force ÷ area
   600 ÷ 0.8 = 750 N/m²
   (1 mark for correct answer, 1 mark for unit)
   Examiner's tip *Make sure you have a calculator that works and that you know how to use it.*
   ii 600 ÷ 30 *(1 mark)*
   = 20 *(1 mark)*
   N/cm² *(1 mark)*
   Examiner's tip *Be careful to work in the correct units.*

7) a) upthrust *(top box)* *(1 mark)*
   weight *(bottom box)* *(1 mark)*
   b) The forces are balanced. *(1 mark)*
   c) float *(no mark)*
   The density of polystyrene is less than the density of water. *(1 mark)*

8) a) i A
   ii C
   iii B *(All correct for 1 mark)*
   b) i Particles gain energy; *(1 mark)*
   regular arrangement breaks down *(1 mark)*
   ii Particles gain more energy; *(1 mark)*
   structure breaks down and moves apart *(1 mark)*

c) Both require energy   *(1 mark)*

d) i   C   *(1 mark)*

   ii   D   *(1 mark)*

   iii   A and B   *(1 mark)*

     Examiner's tip *Answers may be in either order, but* **both** *answers are required for the mark.*

   iv   A and D   *(1 mark)*

     Examiner's tip *Answers may be in either order, but* **both** *answers are required for the mark.*

   v   C   *(1 mark)*

9) a) universal indicator   *(1 mark)*

   b) i   ethanol   *(1 mark)*

      ii   sodium hydroxide solution   *(1 mark)*

      iii   vinegar   *(1 mark)*

   c) pink to colourless   *(1 mark)*

Notes

Notes

Notes

Notes

Notes